Reef Fishes

OF SOUTH-EAST ASIA

Including MARINE INVERTEBRATES AND CORALS

ELIZABETH WOOD & MICHAEL AW

NEW
HOLLAND

This edition published in 2011
First published in 2002 by
New Holland Publishers (UK) Ltd
London • Cape Town • Sydney • Auckland
www.newhollandpublishers.com

Garfield House, 86–88 Edgware Road,
London W2 2EA, United Kingdom

80 McKenzie Street, Cape Town 8001,
South Africa

Unit 1, 66 Gibbes Street, Chatswood,
NSW 2067, Australia

218 Lake Road, Northcote, Auckland,
New Zealand

ISBN 978 1 84773 983 4

Publisher: Simon Papps
Publishing Manager: Jo Hemmings
Project Editor: Camilla MacWhannell
Production Controller: Joan Woodroffe
Editing, cartography and design: D & N
  Publishing, Baydon, Marlborough, Wiltshire
Drawings: Mick Loates

Reproduction by Modern Age Repro House
  Limited, Hong Kong
Printed and bound by Times Offset Sdn Bhd,
Malaysia.

Photographic Acknowledgements
All photographs by Michael Aw with the
exception of the following:
Elizabeth Wood: p29 (middle left), p35 (top
left and right, bottom right), p37 (all photos),
p39 (top left and right), p95 (bottom right).

Photographer's Acknowledgements
Dr. Hanny Batuna and Ineke who got me
started; Dr. Gerry Allen, Dr. Carden Wallace,
David Doubilet and Roger Steen for the
inspiration; Sue Crowe, Graeme Goulay, Robert
Houston for using my work – you have
sustained my livelihood. Chris Lee and Alison
Redhead for looking after the fort while I play in
the field. New Holland Publishing for using my
images in this book. And finally my wife Alison
for caddying additional camera systems.

Author's Acknowledgements
Thanks to the many friends and marine
biological colleagues with whom it has been a
pleasure to dive and study coral reef life.
Coral code reproduced by kind permission of
the Marine Conservation Society
(www.mcsuk.org).

Other books by New Holland include:

A Field Guide to the Birds of South-East Asia
by Craig Robson (£35, ISBN 978 1 84773
341 2).

*A Field Guide to the Mammals of South-East
Asia* by Charles M Francis (£35, ISBN 978
1 84537 735 9).

*A Field Guide to the Reptiles of South-East
Asia* by Indraneil Das (£35, ISBN 978 1
84773 347 4).

*Sea Fishes of the Mediterranean, including
Marine Invertebrates* by Lawson Wood
(£10.99, ISBN 978 1 78009 050 4)

*Sea Fishes and Invertebrates of the North Sea
and English Channel* by Lawson Wood
(£10.99, ISBN 978 1 84773 125 8)

**See www.newhollandpublishers.com
for further details and special offers**

CONTENTS

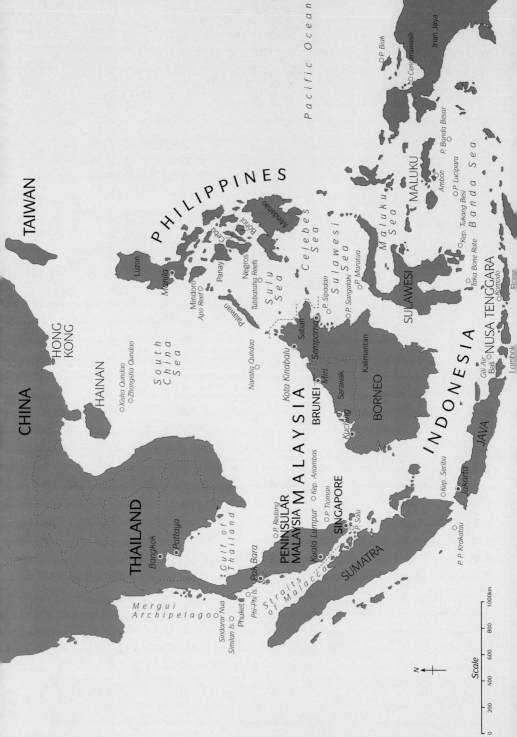

A typical seascape of the region, with a lionfish taking centre stage.

Biodiversity Hot-spot

This book provides a glimpse into the marine life associated with the string of reefs that stretch from Thailand and Taiwan in the north and sweep south and east to Irian Jaya. This extensive archipelago with its tens of thousands of islands straddles the equator and more or less separates the Indian Ocean from the Pacific. In terms of biodiversity, it is acknowledged as the richest in the world, with the centre of diversity lying in the Philippines and Indonesia area. More species occur here than in any other part of the tropical reef world. This is due in part to long-standing favourable climatic conditions and the huge range of habitats associated with the long and varied shorelines. In addition, geological upheavals and sea-level changes have created partial or complete barriers and allowed species to develop in isolation from one another.

Divers see only a tiny proportion of the life occurring on these reefs. Countless species are either too small or too well hidden to be seen. Scientists who censused small organisms occupying holes and crevices in 1 m² (11 sq ft) of reef limestone discovered several hundred thousand organisms belonging to twelve major groups (phyla). Innumerable niches are available, providing endless opportunities for colonization. There are many safe refuges where reef organisms can live and feed, out of the reach of grazers and predators.

Many volumes would be required to describe adequately even the large and conspicuous species that occur in South-east Asian seas. For example, the most diverse reef systems in the region may support over 1,000 species of fish and 400 species of stony corals. On top of that are an indeterminate number of other invertebrates and hundreds of algal species. This book can do little more than provide an introduction to the features of the main groups, and describe a cross-section of the species that are likely to be encountered.

How Reefs Form

Corals are simple anemone-like creatures, which, in the tropics, build substantial geological structures. The reason they can do this is because their living tissues contain symbiotic algae (zooxanthellae), which provide them with extra energy. This helps them to lay down their skeleton relatively quickly.

Fragments of mollusc and crab shell, corals and calcareous algae all contribute to reef formation by filling in holes and irregularities in the reef surface. Undigested material that has passed through the gut of coral-feeding animals does not go to waste either. Tons of sand and fragments reach the surface of the reef in this way, and the fragments become chemically bonded or cemented together to help form a rigid but porous structure. While calcareous forms provide solid material for the reef, soft-bodied organisms, such as sponges, play useful roles by binding coral rubble together to form larger, more stable pieces. They also help to fix these pieces to the reef surface.

The abundance and diversity of life mentioned above is due partly to the unique nature of the coral limestone base. The way that coral skeletons grow, interlock, infill and erode creates habitats of exceptional physical complexity. Although most of the reefs consist of thick accumulations of limestone, other 'reefs' are not strictly coral reefs. For example, the Similan Islands in Thailand are granitic and Komodo in Indonesia is built of volcanic rock, but both support coral communities.

Types of Reef

Fringing Reefs
Fringing reefs develop close to the shore of mainland coastlines and tropical islands and in evolutionary terms are relatively 'young'. This is the commonest type of reef found in South-east Asia. The water above the reef may be very shallow, but in places where the seabed drops away steeply close to the shore it can be hundreds of metres deep. Features include terraces, gentle slopes, spurs, canyons, pinnacles and steep-sided faces. Sometimes the reefs drop downwards in a series of steps or terraces, rather than as a continuous slope or drop-off.

Barrier Reefs
Barrier reefs typically occur on the outer edge of the continental shelf, where the seabed drops abruptly from 100 to 200m (330–660ft) to the deep ocean floor beneath. Some barriers have evolved from fringing reefs, whose position relative to the land has changed, others have a more complicated geological history. There are many small barrier reefs in the region, for example south of Panay in the Philippines and north-east of Kalimantan in Borneo. Indonesia has over 70 barrier reefs scattered throughout the archipelago. One of the largest is in the Gulf of Tomini (northern Sulawesi), where an extensive barrier reef system surrounds most of the Togian Islands

Atolls
'True' atolls occur in oceanic waters, beyond the edge of the continental shelf. The foundation is volcanic rock, on which is a cap of coral limestone thousands of metres thick, with living coral on the very top. Darwin's widely accepted theory is that each atoll started life millions of years ago as a fringing reef around a volcanic island peak. Over time, the island gradually subsided, but the reef kept on growing, forming a circular structure with a lagoon in the middle. About 400 atolls exist in the world's tropical oceans. Many are in the Indian and Pacific oceans, but there are a number in South-east Asian

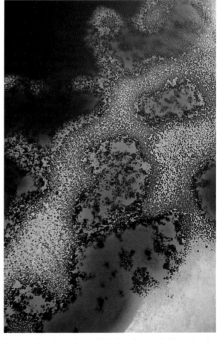

The complex shape of a reef in Indonesia revealed from the air.

seas, especially in the southern part of the region. Taka Bone Rate, the third largest atoll in the world, is situated off the southern coast of Sulawesi.

Other Reef Formations

There are many other reef formations, ranging in size from a few metres to hundreds or thousands of metres in diameter. *Pinnacles*, which are sometimes called 'bommies', are tall and narrow, generally with a diameter of 50m (165ft) or less. They occur either in atoll lagoons or on the slopes of outer reefs. *Patch reefs* may also stand tens of metres above the seabed, but are relatively wide. Large ones several kilometres in diameter are often called *platform reefs*. *Bank reefs* are similar to platform reefs, but their tops may be as much as 40m (130ft) below the surface of the water, with no parts emerging. They may represent 'drowned reefs', and are quite numerous in the South-east Asian region. There are also many *shoals*, for example in the South China Sea, which consist of aggregations of various types of reef lying some distance from the mainland shore.

Snorkler over a reef at Sangalaki, off the Kalimantan coast.

Sand Cays

In many cases, patch reefs break the surface and islands are formed. This happens when waves breaking on the top of the reef produce debris that is then swept onto the reef flat, where it accumulates. Shingle ramparts or banks usually build up on the windward edge, while a sandy islet forms on the sheltered side. These patch reefs are then usually referred to as sand cay reefs or simply cays.

Reef Zones

Tropical reefs have a biological origin, with corals as the major component. Corals and other reef organisms respond in particular ways to light, water movement and other environmental factors. This produces a basic layout or zonation from the shore or shallow water down to the base of the reef slope. All reefs have a top, an edge and a slope, but within this there is great variation. The top may be a pinnacle or flat expanse of coral, the edge sharp or ill-defined, and the slope gentle or dramatically precipitous. The depth of the reef below the water surface varies from a few metres to hundreds of metres and the profile from a virtually horizontal platform to a vertical cliff. These differences reflect the geological history and state of development of the reef, the slope and depth of the underlying seabed, and the degree of exposure to waves, currents and biological erosion.

The following main zones can be recognized on most reefs:

Back Reef A shallow, sheltered zone situated between the shore and the lagoon or seaward reef. Typical habitats include seagrass beds, rubble and sand patches, eroded limestone slabs and small coral outcrops.

Lagoon A mostly sandy-floored area between the back reef and the inner reef flat of barrier reefs or atolls. The depth varies from about 1–100m (3–330ft). Typical habitats include sand, seagrass beds, rubble and limestone slabs, coral micro-atolls, knolls, pinnacles and patch reefs.

Reef Flat Extremely shallow (0–1m/0–3ft in depth), intertidal area between the lagoon and the seaward reef front. This zone may be very extensive on some barrier reefs and atolls, with large areas exposed at low tide. Typical habitats include sea-grass beds, coral-filled tide-pools, coral micro-atolls and eroded limestone platforms with sand, rubble and small live corals.

Spillways, Channels and Passages These formations are gulleys of varying depths. Spillways are very shallow; they drain the reef flat, but are not permanently open. Channels and passages connect the lagoon to the open sea. They vary in width and depth but are open at all states of the tide. Typical habitats include passage walls, which are

Sea grass beds are very rich habitats to explore.

(Below) Diver under an overhang.

often rich with reef life, and in contrast the gully floor, which is often scoured and bare.

Shallow Fore-reef This is the upper part of the seaward-facing reef, to a depth of about 15–20m (50–65ft). The reef may curve either gently or steeply, and sometimes there are steps or terraces present. Typical habitats here include algal ridges, spur and groove formations, coral and rock outcrops, and sand patches. This is usually the area with the highest diversity and cover of reef-building corals.

Deep Fore-reef This includes the lower part of the seaward-facing reef, from about 15–20m (50–65ft) downwards. The slope may be gentle or steep and typical habitats include walls, sand and rubble chutes, underhangs, ledges, caves and canyons.

Classification – What's in a Name?

Common names are used as much as possible throughout this book, but this can be a drawback because some species are called different things by different people and this leads to confusion. Many organisms do not even have a common name. On the other hand, a scientific name is unique and, however difficult to pronounce or remember, cannot be muddled with anything else.

A scientific name has two parts: the first part states the genus to which the organism has been assigned and the second part the species. Organisms that are not sexually compatible, but have many close similarities, are placed in the same genus. Sometimes a genus has only a single species in it, but usually there are several. For example, most of the larger groupers are in the genus *Epinephelus*, while other members of the family have slightly different features and are put into other genera, such as *Cephalopholis* and *Serranus*.

The species' name completes the description and identifies that particular entity as one in which individuals are sexually compatible and produce fertile offspring. Nearly all the examples selected for this book are identified to species, but where there is uncertainty or the organism has not yet been described by taxonomists, then it will simply be called, for example, *Antipathes* sp. There are a number of groups in the region (e.g. soft corals and sponges) that have such a bewildering array of species that it will be some years before taxonomists can describe and put a name to all of them.

Scientific names are generally based on Latin or Greek words, and conventionally they are written in italics. The scientists who describe the species select a name which may be descriptive of the organism concerned or named after the person who found it, or the geographic location or habitat where it was first found. Sometimes apparently nonsense names are chosen – such as *Abudefduf*. The common name is often a translation of the scientific one; thus *Octopus vulgaris* is the Common Octopus.

Reef Conservation and the Tourist's 'Coral Code'

It is well known that coral reefs around the world are facing numerous threats and that many have been damaged, degraded and over-exploited. There are many ways in which this can happen, and activities on land are to blame in some cases: corals and other reef inhabitants have been damaged and killed by dirty and polluted water and by sediment; coastal developments and run-off from the land are common causes of pollution and siltation; and sewage and other organic wastes are also causing particular problems for reefs.

Destructive fishing methods, anchoring and boat collisions are also all taking their toll. Corals are

An exposed reef flat at low tide. Such areas can sometimes be extensive.

Damage to the reef and its inhabitants caused by fishing with explosives.

slow-growing and, if damaged or removed, may take years to recover. In addition, the reef environment is being changed, degraded and destroyed by coastal developments, harbours, jetties and sea walls. Reef tourism brings benefits, such as employment and foreign currency, but reefs are suffering from trampling, anchors and other impacts from intensive use.

Many reefs have been overfished, and destructive fishing methods, such as fish blasting, are wasteful and also damage the reef habitat. Equally worrying is the fact that reefs seem to be becoming more susceptible to disease, perhaps partly because of the stress they are under. On top of all these woes comes coral bleaching, which in most cases is associated with thermal stress and is probably related to global warming caused by human-induced atmospheric pollution.

Much will be lost if reefs become further damaged. Their value as fishing grounds, sources of medicinal compounds, tourist attractions, natural self-repairing breakwaters and places of scientific interest will disappear. Many people depend on healthy reefs to make a livelihood, and their prosperity and way of life could be put in jeopardy if reef health and productivity decline.

A successful tourist industry relies on healthy reefs if it is to prosper. Yet tourism can easily damage the resource on which it depends. Construction of hotels and pontoons, demand for fresh seafood and souvenirs from the reef, and the activities of snorkellers, divers and boats all have an impact.

As tourists, we can do much to help reefs by acting responsibly and supporting conservation organizations, such as the Marine Conservation Society, a UK-based charity that has produced the following Coral Code:

Planning your Holiday/Making Choices
◆ When you book your holiday, try to choose a destination where active reef management is in place – such as a marine park.
◆ Ask your tour operator if they have an environmental policy. Enquire if – and how – they support reef conservation.
◆ Find out if the tour operators explain the 'dos and don'ts' to people before they visit the reef. It has been shown that a short briefing can dramatically cut the amount of damage caused by divers and snorkellers.
◆ Make sure you play your part too, not just underwater but on land. Try to minimize impact, for example by being sparing with freshwater, using biodegradable shampoos and disposing of litter in the correct way – even bringing it back home if necessary.

Looking for Souvenirs
◆ Collection of souvenirs from the reef is prohibited in many areas – please respect all local and international laws.

◆ Hard corals, black corals, marine turtles, queen conch, and all their products are protected under CITES (the Convention on International Trade in Endangered Species) and can be bought and sold only with a licence.
◆ Resist the temptation to buy other marine curios. In most cases insufficient is known about the harvesting operations to be certain they are sustainable – take the safe route and buy alternative souvenirs.

Going Paddling, Snorkelling or Diving
◆ Keep to designated walkways or sand channels when in shallow reef areas. Feet and fins can easily break and damage the reef top.
◆ Maintain perfect buoyancy control when diving so as to keep clear of the reef.
◆ Never stand, sit or rest on living corals. Despite having hard skeletons, part or all of the colony may die from infection if the delicate outer soft tissues are injured.
◆ If you need to steady yourself use finger tips on bare rock – leave your gloves behind.
◆ Avoid kicking up sand. It may settle on corals and other reef animals and suffocate them.
◆ Enjoy taking a close look at reef life, but don't touch, move or molest animals for amusement or photography.
◆ Be satisfied with nature as it is. Fish feeding may have a place in a few selected areas but generally is not encouraged. It disrupts natural behaviour and can upset the ecological balance of species on reefs.

Using a Boat
◆ When visiting the reef, always use a mooring buoy, jetty or pontoon if one is provided. Urge boat operators and authorities to consider installing buoys at frequently visited sites.
◆ Never anchor on corals. They are easily broken or damaged by anchors and anchor chains.
◆ Reconnoitre carefully before stopping. Polaroid sunglasses make it easier to pick out seabed features. Find a sand or rubble patch and drop anchor carefully. Make sure the anchor is not dragging on to the reef.

Dangers of the Reef
By and large, coral reefs are safe places to explore. Most of the accidents that occur are connected with diving procedures and equipment rather than encounters with dangerous marine life. However, it is wise to be aware of, and avoid, certain species or situations that can lead to discomfort, injury, and – very rarely – to death.

The reef is a crowded place where the inhabitants compete with each other for space and where much of life revolves around eating or avoiding being eaten. There are many mechanisms for catching food and for avoiding being eaten or grown over, including the ability to bite or sting for defence and offence, and the use of chemicals that poison or deter would-be attackers. Sometimes these chemicals are by-products of metabolic processes, but whatever their derivation, they can have a powerful effect. If divers happen to touch animals that deploy toxins or get in the way of fish with sharp teeth then they may regret it. Heat or vinegar are often good antidotes to stings because they denature the poison.

The following animals are capable of injuring humans:

Sharks generally only attack humans when divers are spearfishing or carrying bait.

Stingrays will only sting if trodden on or caught.

Barracuda might possibly attack in murky water if misled by reflective gear into thinking a diver is their normal prey.

Moray eels will readily bite divers who inadvertently put their hands into their den.

Stonefish do not attack, but are well camouflaged and may be trodden on, causing intense pain from their highly venomous spines.

Triggerfish Nesting males are aggressive and will charge and bite divers who get too close.

Jellyfish Most species have stinging tentacles. The small sea wasps are especially painful and dangerous.

Fire coral (*Millepora* spp.) inflicts a nasty sting if divers brush up against it.

Hydroids Most have a painful sting and may cause long-lasting wheals.

Cone shells Use strong toxins to disable their prey and will also 'inject' humans with it if they are handled.

Sea urchins have spines, which are toxic in some species and can cause considerable pain if they penetrate the skin.

Distribution and Features of South-East Asian Reefs

Thailand

In Thailand, the best area for reefs is off the west coast in the Andaman Sea, although development is restricted almost entirely to the offshore islands. The deepest reefs are at the southern end of the Mergui Archipelago, running from Sindarar in the north to the Similan Islands in the south. Islands further south, such as Phuket and Phi-Phi (and others in Phangnga Bay) have shallow reefs and well-developed coral communities. Patch and fringing reefs occur around islands off Pak Bara (Tarutao National Park) in the south, adjacent to the border with Malaysia. Phuket and the Similan Islands are major centres for diving.

In the Gulf of Thailand fringing reefs occur around some of the 100 or so islands, including Koh Samui, Cumphon, Ang Thong National Marine Park and Mu Koh Chang Marine Park. Coral diversity is relatively low and the water tends to be turbid, but some diving is carried out, for example at Pattaya.

China

Conditions along the mainland coast of China are too cool and turbid for reef development. Fringing reefs and coral communities occur on the southern coastline of the island of Hainan, but the best reef development is around islands further offshore. Some of the most extensive reefs occur around Xisha Qundao (Paracel Shoals), Zhongsha Qundao (Macclesfield Bank: two atolls) and Nansha Qundao (Spratly Islands). East of Hong Kong is the atoll of Dongsha Qundao and south of this the oceanic atoll Huangyan (Tung-sha reef). Diving the outlying reefs is not easy because of their isolation and because many lie in disputed territory.

Hong Kong

Hong Kong is near the northern limit of climatic conditions suitable for coral growth, with water temperatures dropping to 15°C in winter. Also floodwater and sediments (e.g. influx of water from the Pearl River in the west) produce conditions that are not ideal for coral growth. Few corals occur below a depth of 10m (33ft). The richest communities are in the north-east where the water is cleaner. Diving is popular.

Taiwan

Fringing reefs and coral communities occur around the Hengchun Peninsula, at the southern tip of Taiwan. They are present on all except the sandy west coast and, despite fairly turbid water and the impact of monsoons, show high species diversity. Offshore islands such as Lu-tao (Green Island) also have quite extensive fringing reefs.

Philippines

There are more than 7,000 islands in the Philippines that have extensive reef development in the form of fringing and patch reefs, but also banks and shoals, a few small barrier reefs (e.g. south of Panay and north of Bohol) and atolls (e.g. Scarborough Reef, west of Luzon in the South China Sea; Apo Reef, west of Mindoro; Tubbataha and others in the Sulu Sea).

Reefs around Palawan, Cebu and Negros are amongst the best for diving, and include drop-offs (e.g. Balicasag and Panglao Islands south of Bohol). Philippine reefs have been stressed as a result of sedimentation, over-fishing and dynamite fishing, but many conservation initiatives are now underway.

Malaysia

In general, coral patches and fringing reefs occur only sporadically along mainland coastlines of Malaysia. The main reef development is around offshore islands. In Peninsular Malaysia, islands such as Tioman and Redang off the east coast have the best reefs and are popular dive areas.

In Sabah (East Malaysia) shallow reefs fringe the 40 or so islands off the west coast and there are precipitous deep reefs further offshore around Pu Layang-Layang (part of the Spratly Islands) and along the edge of the continental shelf facing into the South China Sea. All these sites are dived.

The best reef development off Sabah's east coast is in the south, where there are patch and fringing reefs around the islands off Semporna, a small barrier reef and an oceanic seamount (Pu Sipadan) with a dramatic, precipitous reef, very popular with divers.

The mainland coast of Sarawak has coral communities, but coastal waters are generally too shallow and turbid for reefs to develop. However, there are extensive reefs offshore from Miri, including the Luconia Shoals.

Singapore

The waters around Singapore are shallow and relatively turbid, but support some fringing and patch reefs, especially around the southern islands. Pu Salu is completely surrounded by reef and is one of the richest reef areas in Singapore waters.

Indonesia

Indonesia is a huge country with over 13,660 islands. Large parts of Java and Sumatra are unsuited to reef development because of river inflow and sediments, but elsewhere there are extensive reefs.

KALIMANTAN

A barrier reef occurs offshore in the north-east of Kalimantan, where there is a string of islands with extensive reefs including Kakaban (with its enclosed jellyfish lake), Derawan, Sangalaki and Maratua. Far offshore from the west coast (most easily accessed from Singapore) is the Anambas Island group, with its many fringing reefs.

SUMATRA

Stretches of fringing reef occur around the chain of islands running along the west coast of Sumatra, and there are scattered reefs off the east coast.

JAVA

Coral reefs and communities occur on the islands between Java and Sumatra, including the volcanic Krakatoa Islands. These sites are accessible to divers. Fringing reefs occur around many of the 110 islands of the Seribu Archipelago in Jakarta Bay. Diving is well established here, but the reefs and visibility are only of average quality.

Kakaban, off the north-east coast of Kalimantan, with its enclosed jellyfish lake.

(Below) Pu Sipadan is an oceanic seamount off Sabah.

Coral growth on a wreck off Tulamben, Bali.

BALI

Bali has many good areas of fringing reef, especially along the north and east coast (e.g. Amed and Tulamben). The reefs around the small island of Menjangan (north-east) are particularly spectacular, with caves, steep faces and healthy corals. There are many diving centres on Bali.

NUSA TENGGARA

These south-eastern islands of the Indonesian archipelago are a mixture of volcanic (some still active) and limestone islands. Shallow fringing reefs at Gili are amongst the most accessible, and also the reefs around Flores, including Komodo at the western end. In the Bay of Maumere there are reefs with steep walls and excellent marine life. The island of Alor off central Timor has similarly rich reefs with prolific fish life. Tukang Besi Archipelago in the north-east is similarly diverse. Taka Bone Rate has some spectacular reefs, but some areas that are damaged, and is visited occasionally by dive boats.

MALUKU (MOLUCCAS)

Maluku consists of numerous large and small islands with extensive reefs. The more isolated reefs in particular are in pristine condition, for example around the Lucipara Islands in the Banda Sea. Diving operations in Maluku are at the early stages of development, but it is possible to dive around Ambon and the Banda Islands. The latter have a range of reef sites from shallow lagoons to precipitous walls.

IRIAN JAYA

Irian Jaya has some fringing reefs in the south, but the most extensive reef development is off the north coast, in the vicinity of Cenderawasih Bay. Some of the bay reefs have been damaged by fish blasting, but there are excellent undamaged reefs around Biak Island, where a live-aboard dive boat is based. Many small islands rise from deep water, including the Padaido Islands, Budd Island and Mapia Island (an atoll); dramatic diving can be had here, with walls and many fish.

KEY TO SYMBOLS

This key describes the symbols that appear at the head of each species description. The symbols give a quick guide for the habit, diet and habitat of each species.

Habit	*Diet*	*Habitat*
single	algae	caves
pairs	plankton	seagrass
groups	invertebrates	sand
schools	mixed corals	reefs
	fish	pelagic

This diagram illustrates the main structures of a fish referred to in the species descriptions.

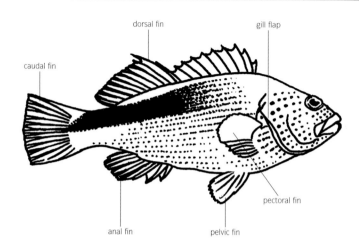

IDENTIFICATION GROUPS AND PICTORIAL GUIDE TO FAMILIES

Colour varies greatly between fish species, therefore it would seem an ideal means of identification. However, even within species, colour varies according to sex, age, region, season and surroundings. For this reason, body shape is a much more reliable means of identification. The following outlines represent all types of fish likely to be encountered in the South China Sea. Those sharing similar characteristics are grouped together for initial identification.

RAYS AND SHARKS

Whale shark p.54

Zebra shark p.54

Requiem or whaler shark p.56

Stingray p.56

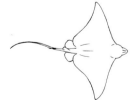

Eagle ray p.56

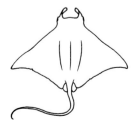

Manta p.58

SILVERY, TORPEDO-SHAPED FISH

Tuna p.132

REGULAR-SHAPED FISH SWIMMING CLOSE TO OR ABOVE REEF

Trevally pp.84

Snapper p.86

Fusilier p.88

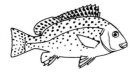

Sweetlips pp.88–90

Spinecheek p.90

Emperor pp.90–92

Chub p.94

ELONGATE FISH SWIMMING CLOSE TO OR ABOVE REEF

Catfish p.62

Garfish p.64

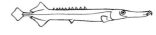

Trumpetfish p.66

Flutemouth p.68

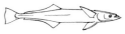

Remora p.84

Barracuda p.118

ELONGATE FISH CLOSE TO OR ON REEF SURFACE

Moray p.58

Snake eel p.60

Garden eel p.60

Lizardfish p.62

Pipefish p.70

Sand tilefish p.82

Jawfish p.116

Sandperch p.118

Triplefin p.120

Sand-diver p.120

Blenny pp.120–122

Dragonet pp.122–124

Dartfish p.124

Goby pp.124–126

REGULAR-SHAPED FISH THAT SWIM WITH PECTORALS

Hogfish p.108

Wrasse pp.108–114

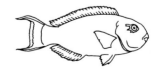

Parrotfish pp.116–118

COLOURFUL REGULAR-SHAPED FISH CLOSE TO REEF

Anthias p.74

Grouper and soapfish pp.76–78

Longfin and prettyfin p.78

Dottyback p.78

Hawkfish p.80

Cardinalfish pp.80–82

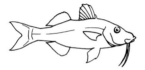

Goatfish p.92

Damselfish and anemonefish pp.102-108

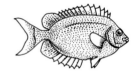

Rabbitfish p.130

IRREGULARLY SHAPED FISH

Clingfish p.62

Frogfish p.64

Razorfish p.68

Ghost Pipefish p.68

Seahorse p.70

Flatheads p.70

Scorpionfish p.72

Lionfish p.72

Flounder p.132

COLOURFUL IRREGULARLY-SHAPED FISH

Batfish p.94

Bannerfish p.98 and Moorish idol p.126

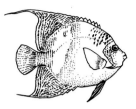

Angelfish p.100

Unicornfish p.130

Triggerfish, filefish and leatherjacket pp.132–136

Trunkfish p.136

Boxfish p.136

Pufferfish p.138

Porcupinefish p.138

COLOURFUL OVAL-SHAPED FISH

Butterflyfish pp.96–98

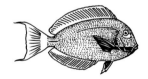

Surgeonfish p.128–130

BIG-EYED FISH OFTEN IN CAVES

Soldierfish p.66

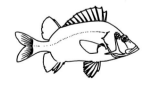

Squirrelfish p.66

Bigeye p.82

Sweeper p.94

SEAGRASSES

Seagrasses are the only flowering plants to occur in the sea, but the flowers are very small and inconspicuous in comparison with those produced by most land plants. For example, those of turtle grass appear in spring and summer, but are hidden out of sight at the base of the stem and only occur in about 1–5 per cent of all plants. The main method of spreading is by root-like runners (rhizomes), which also anchor the plants in the sand. Around 16 species occur in the region.

1 CYMODOCEA SERRULATA

This species has strap-like leaves at least 4mm (⅙in) wide. It is found mainly in the subtidal zone just to the seaward of mangroves, growing in anything from silty mud to coarse coral rubble. Dense stands may be formed, and are remarkably rich habitats to explore. The leaves are often encrusted with small organisms such as sponges, seasquirts and anemones, while flatworms, molluscs and small crabs crawl around amongst the stems. Various juvenile fish spend their young lives in these sheltered surroundings away from the larger reef predators, and there are also fish, such as snake eels, that live here permanently. *Cymodocea* is known to be a food for Dugong. Seagrass beds play an important ecological 'cleansing' role because the tall leaves slow down water movement to such an extent that small particles suspended in the water no longer stay afloat but sink to the sea bed.

ALGAE

Algae are widespread and common on and around reefs, but they are often overlooked because they are smaller and less flamboyant than the animals. Some are single-celled, and live by the tens of thousands inside hard and soft corals and other reef animals, such as Giant Clams. Others are filamentous or tufty, and grow as a 'turf' on rocks and at the base of corals. These types are usually cropped like a well-kept lawn by fish, snails, sea urchins and other grazing animals. There are also larger, more obvious species to be found. Algae are divided into green, brown and red varieties according to the type of pigment they contain. There are many hundreds of species in the region.

2 SEA PEARL or SAILOR'S EYEBALLS
Ventricaria ventricosa

An interesting green alga, occurring in shady places, in shallow water and to depths of well over 60m (200ft). It is easily recognized on both Indo-Pacific and Caribbean reefs. It may grow solitarily or in clusters, with each sphere attached by minute hair-like rhizoids. The spheres, resembling shiny marbles, are up to 5cm (2in) in diameter, yet each is only a single cell – one of the largest cells known in the natural world. *Ventricaria* is very tough, making it unattractive to herbivores. Young cells have a bluish-green, shiny appearance, but older ones are usually covered by epiphytes, such as encrusting sea-mats.

3 GRAPE ALGA
Caulerpa racemosa

A number of the green seaweeds seen in shallow, sandy areas belong to the genus *Caulerpa*. They all have flattish rhizomes and root-like rhizoids that spread out over sand, rubble or rocks, and prevent the alga being dislodged. The rhizomes give off vertical stems, which themselves bear smaller branchlets or 'leaves'. Grape Alga is one of the relatively few plant species that occurs throughout tropical seas. It grows up to 15cm (6in) tall and is unmistakable because the tips of the branchlets are rounded, and massed together they look like clusters of tiny green grapes. This species is common in shallow rocky areas, particularly where there is some wave surge.

1 *Cymodocea serrulata*

2 Sea Pearl

3 Grape Alga

1 HANGING VINE

Halimeda spp.

Many species of the green alga *Halimeda* occur in the region. All have fronds consisting of small, round or heart-shaped, calcified disks, which are joined to each other by a narrow strand. Some species form tufts, but others hang downwards from the holdfast and may form long branching chains. When the plants die, they turn white as the calcium deposits in their tissues are exposed. Piles of disintegrating calcified disks can often be seen adding to the accumulations of sand around reefs. Apart from being calcareous and so 'crunchy' for would-be grazers, *Halimeda* produces compounds (diterpenoids) that have been shown experimentally to deter fish from feeding.

2 FUNNELWEED

Padina gymospora

Padina species have fan-shaped blades with an in-rolled outer margin. They have a characteristically pale appearance, due to deposits of calcium carbonate on the upper surface of the blade. As in other species of *Padina,* the concentric lines on the blade are formed from rows of microscopic hairs alternating with reproductive structures. Funnelweed is common in many habitats, but is especially abundant on shallow reef flats.

3 CALCAREOUS RED ALGAE

Throughout the reef, there are many genera and hence species of calcareous red algae. Typically, these algae form thin crusts that follow the contours of the rock. Other growth forms range from solid nodules to dense masses of criss-crossing branches. On steep slopes the algae may become plate-like with free outer edges sometimes overlapping like tiles. It is also common to come across unattached specimens living on the surface of sand or rubble, especially towards the base of the reef slope. They are usually either brownish, dark red or burgundy, and often have white margins. Calcareous algae may dominate reef surfaces in certain situations; for example they may be so abundant in wave-exposed shallow areas that they build a ridge (algal crest) where the water breaks. Calcareous red algae play an important ecological role in helping to build and consolidate reefs.

SPONGES

Sponges have no sensory or nervous system and no specialized internal organs, but despite their simplicity they are extremely successful animals. They are effective filtering machines, using tiny whip-like flagellae to create a current of water, which is drawn into the body through small pores. Plankton, micro-organisms and small nutritious particles of debris are removed from the flow of water, and the water then exits through a hole called the osculum. This excurrent opening is invariably larger than the in-going pores, and is usually situated at the highest point of the animal, so that waste water is more effectively carried away. Sponges often contain substances that act as deterrents to animals that might try to feed on them. Many of these compounds are biologically active, and are of considerable interest to the pharmaceutical industry in their quest for new drugs.

Several hundred species of sponge probably occur in the region, but many have yet to be described and named. Identification of sponges is complicated because individual species may have different growth forms and colour in response to differing environmental conditions. Species may closely resemble one another in general appearance, and positive identification can be made only by laboratory examination of the tiny 'spicules' of silica or calcium that form the skeleton. The few examples shown here are all reasonably easy to identify and illustrate the range of growth forms that may be encountered, including tubes, vases, crusts, barrels and ropes. Most of them do not have common names.

1 Hanging vine *(above and above right)*

2 Funnelweed

3 Calcareous red algae *(below)*

1 *MONANCHORA UNGICULATA*

Many sponges are brightly coloured, perhaps as a warning to predators that they are unpalatable. *M. ungiculata* is a vivid red, branching species that occurs mainly on sheltered, silty reef slopes. It can change its shape and sometimes deflates to form a fairly thin layer over the reef surface. It occurs sporadically throughout the region.

2 TUBE SPONGE

Kalypilidion fascigera

Two of the many species of tube sponge are shown here – *Mycale* sp. in the foreground and *Kalypilidion fascigera* behind. The latter may occur as a single tube, but more usually there are several together. The tubes can reach a height of about 1m (3ft 3in), and are up to 5cm (2in) in diameter. They are a striking pale pink or blue in colour. The outer surface of the tubes is covered in small, spikey protuberances. It is commonly found on reef slopes throughout the region.

3 ROPE SPONGE

Haliclona sp.

Several species of sponge form rope-like growths that straggle over the surface of the reef, sometimes producing quite large clumps. *Haliclona* is distinctive because of its deep blue colour and the presence of several large oscula on each branch. It occurs mainly in shallow areas and is found throughout the region.

4 BARREL SPONGE

Xestospongia testudinaria

This unmistakable species reaches a height of 1m (3ft) or more. It grows slowly, and large specimens are probably over 100 years old. The outside is covered with vertical ridges or knobbly protuberances. These long-lived sponges provide shelter and vantage points for many other animals, such as zoanthids, brittlestars, small

holothurians and fishes. Despite their hard structure, the rim of the barrel is quite brittle and easily damaged if divers – and some have been known to do it – try to climb inside. The barrel sponge is fairly common throughout the region, usually at depths from 5–40m (15–130ft).

5 FAN SPONGE

Ianthella basta

This sponge forms very thin fan-like fronds that have narrow, vertical ridges on the surface. It grows to 1m (3ft) or more in height, and its colour is very variable, ranging from yellow to green and dark purple. It is found mainly on wave-sheltered reef slopes with some current, at depths of about 10–20m (33–65ft). This species occurs throughout the region but has rather a patchy distribution. However, where conditions are favourable it may be present in large numbers.

6 *LEUCETTA CHAGOSENSIS*

This is an example of a sponge in which the spicules are calcareous rather than siliceous. There are relatively few calcareous sponges, and all are small species that tend to be found in shady areas on the reef slope. *L. chagosensis* forms conspicuous, bright yellow colonies that are irregular but basically globular. They are solid and compact due to the tightly packed mass of internal spicules embedded in a matrix of spongy fibres. Widespread in the Indo-Pacific.

7 ENCRUSTING SPONGE

Clathria mima

Like many of the other species of encrusting sponge that occur in the area, the pattern of channels leading to the exhalant siphons are clearly visible. In this species they are white or pale, and stand out against the deep red of the rest of the sponge. *C. mima* occurs in sheltered situations on the reef slope. Widespread throughout the region and in the Western Pacific.

Sponges

1 *Monanchora ungiculata (far left)*

2 Tube sponge *(left)*

3 Rope sponge *(above)*

4 Barrel sponge

5 Fan sponge *(right)*

6 *Leucetta chagosensis*

7 Encrusting sponge

CNIDARIANS

Cnidarians include anemones, jellyfish, sea fans, sea whips, corals and many others. They are hugely important reef animals, with thousands of species occurring in the region. The body layout is quite simple, with two tissue layers, but no internal organs. There are two basic body forms: the attached polyp and the floating medusa. Some sub-groups within the phylum have both forms represented during their life history, or one may predominate over the other. The typical polyp is anemone-like, consisting of a tube closed at the attached end and a mouth and surrounding ring of tentacles at the other. Food is captured by the tentacles and passed through the mouth into the internal cavity where it is digested. Wastes exit through the mouth. The medusa is bell-shaped with a central mouth and usually tentacles around the perimeter.

A feature of cnidarians is that they are armed with stinging cells, which are used in defence and also to catch prey. These cnidae (nematocysts) are too small to be seen with the naked eye, but their effect can be felt on human skin. Cnidarians reproduce sexually, producing floating larvae (planula) that colonize new areas. In most species within the group, polyps divide or bud to produce new polyps, which remain attached, so forming a colony. A large hard or soft coral colony may consist of thousands of polyps, all of which originate from the settlement of a single planula.

There are four classes and many sub-groups within the cnidarians, some of which are briefly described and illustrated in the following pages.

HYDROZOANS

The typical hydroid is an attached colony with a feathery or fern-like growth form. The polyps are tiny, but in most species they have a powerful sting. During sexual reproduction many hydroids produce a tiny jellyfish called a hydromedusa, but this is too small to be noticed by divers, and is also very short lived.

1 STINGING HYDROID
Aglaophenia cupressina
Many hydroids are small and relatively inconspicuous, but the stinging hydroid grows to a height of about 30cm (1ft) so cannot be overlooked. It grows as a cluster of stems that have alternately arranged branches along their length. These branches bear secondary branchlets on which the tiny white polyps are situated. The small dots seen on the branches are reproductive structures. *A. cupressina* is beautiful to look at but has a very painful sting. It is common on reefs throughout the region, from shallow water to depths of about 30m (100ft).

2 FIRE CORAL
Millepora sp.
Millepora is one of a number of hydroids that produces a calcareous skeleton. The others

(*Stylaster* and *Distichopora*) are small, delicate and brightly coloured, but *Millepora* forms large colonies that are important reef builders. *Millepora* species are known as fire corals because of their painful sting. This sting is inflicted by batteries of nematocysts on the long, hair-like polyps (dactylozooids) whose main function is defence. The dactylozooids surround much shorter, stouter polyps that have a mouth and are responsible for capturing and ingesting prey. Fire corals are distinguished from stony corals by their smooth appearance, pale brown colour and microscopic polyps. They are found in most reef habitats throughout the region.

3 LACE CORAL
Stylaster sp.
This beautiful and delicate colony is also a calcified hydrozoan, but unlike *Millepora* species it does not sting. It typically forms very delicate colonies with fine, tapering branches. Its colour ranges from purple to pink, and the branch ends are paler. Polyps are situated in tiny cups, which can just be made out, scattered over the branches. Lace coral is common throughout the region and is found mainly on clear, seaward reefs, especially in sheltered, shaded habitats, such as underhangs and crevices, and on the deep reef slope.

1 Stinging hydroid

2 Fire coral *(above)*   **3** Lace coral *(below)*

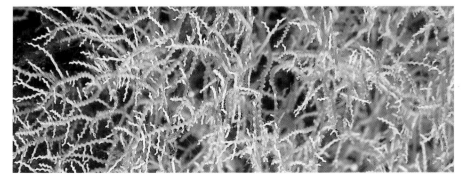

SCYPHOZOANS

This Class contains the 'true' jellyfish, which spend all their time afloat as medusae. The bell varies greatly in shape and size, as does the number and length of tentacles that occur around its margin. The mouth is at the end of a tube, which often has frilly 'oral lobes' around it. Jellyfish can swim by pulsating the bell, but they are largely at the mercy of ocean currents, and may get washed ashore in large numbers. Sea wasps are a different type of jellyfish that belong in the Class Cubozoa. They are distinguished by having a square bell with bundles of tentacles at each corner.

1 UPSIDE-DOWN JELLYFISH
Cassiopea andromeda
Upside-down Jellyfish have a saucer-shaped bell up to 15cm (6in) in diameter, and oral arms that branch into thousands of tiny frills. These are packed with microscopic unicellular algae (zooxanthellae) and the jellyfish gains much of its nutrition from this symbiotic relationship. It is for this reason that the jellyfish 'sunbathe' upside down, to expose the algae to maximum light. When on the move they swim in the normal way, with the bell uppermost. The sting may be quite painful. This species occurs throughout the region.

ANTHOZOANS – OCTOCORALS

Anthozoans are represented only by the polyp stage. There are many taxonomic divisions within the Class, containing a range of familiar animals such as soft corals, sea fans, anemones, black corals and sea pens. Some are known as octocorals because the polyps have eight tentacles. These are branched, giving the polyp a feathery appearance. Others, the hexacorals, have six or a multiple of six tentacles associated with each polyp, and these are normally unbranched.

The octocorals consist of four main groups: stoloniferans, alcyonarians (soft corals), gorgonians (sea fans and sea whips) and pennatulaceans (sea pens). Each of these is illustrated in the following pages.

2 ORGANPIPE CORAL
Tubipora musica
The Organpipe Coral is an example of a stoloniferan, but it is unlike other species within the group because the polyps are enclosed within calcareous tubes. The red or purple tubes are just a few millimetres in diameter, and are stacked closely in an upright position. They are linked by horizontal plates, which can sometimes be seen if the colony has split apart or, more likely, has been cast up on the beach. Colonies are rounded and up to about 50cm (1ft 8in) in diameter. Greenish coloured polyps with eight petal-like tentacles are usually extended during the day. It occurs throughout the region and wider Indo-Pacific, on shallow reefs to depths of about 15m (50ft).

3 MUSHROOM SOFT CORAL
Sarcophyton spp.
Sarcophyton is one of the more familiar of the numerous soft corals (alcyonarians) that occur in the region. Typical of other soft corals, the colony is supported and strengthened by thousands of tiny calcareous spicules that are embedded in the fleshy tissue. Species of the genus *Sarcophyton* form characteristic bowl or mushroom-shaped colonies, which have a stout stem and an expanded top from which the polyps protrude. The polyps are generally extended during the day. Like some other cnidarians it can deflate its body and then pump it up again by drawing in water. These soft corals feed on zooplankton, but also obtain nourishment from their stock of symbiotic zooxanthellae. They are common throughout the region.

4 *SINULARIA* spp.
Numerous species of *Sinularia* (alcyonarians) occur in the region, but they are difficult to identify to species. Many form thick, encrusting colonies, but others have lobes and some species are tall and bushy. They are often rather a drab brown colour due to the presence in their tissues of microscopic algae (zooxanthellae). They are successful colonists of shallow reefs, partly due to their ability to use chemical warfare. For example, some species can retard the growth of coral from as much as 30cm (1ft) away, without any physical contact. They do this by releasing toxic chemicals that spread through the water. *Sinularia* spp. are common throughout the region.

1 Upside-down Jellyfish

2 Organpipe Coral

3 Mushroom soft coral

4 *Sinularia* spp. *(above and right)*

Cnidarians

1 SOFT CORAL
Dendronephthya sp.
Dendronephthya is a striking soft coral that is profusely branched, forming bushy or tree-like colonies that are often pink or reddish in colour. The colonies are attached by a stout stem and may grow in profusion on steep slopes and shady overhangs. Minute crystalline structures (sclerites) are embedded in the tissues, providing support but allowing the colonies to expand and retract. Some sclerites may protrude from the surface of the colony, giving the colony a prickly appearance. Several species of *Dendronephthya* occur in the area, but their taxonomy is still uncertain.

2 SEA FAN
Semperina sp.
Semperina is one example of a gorgonian sea fan. Many other genera occur in the area, and they range in size from under 10cm (4in) to several metres in height. Gorgonians differ from soft corals in having a solid, rod-like central core consisting of a horny material called gorgonin. Sea fans have strong, flexible stems that branch profusely, usually in one plane, to form a delicate meshwork. They do not have zooxanthellae in their tissues and so need to maximize the chances of planktonic food passing close to the polyps. Thus they are found in situations with some water movement, where they align themselves at right angles to the current flow. They are found throughout the region.

3 SEA WHIP
Elisella spp.
Sea whips form unbranched or sparsely branched stems that are long and stiff, yet flexible. They often occur in clumps, formed as a result of asexual reproduction. As the sea whips grow, small pieces are pinched off at the tops. This feat is achieved as a result of degeneration of tissues along a small portion of the whip until only the central, horny rod remains. This then gets broken off by water movement, drops on to the reef surface, cements and grows. The polyps of sea whips are small and have eight, branched tentacles. They are found throughout the region.

4 SEA PEN
Virgularia sp.
Sea pens are highly specialized octocorals that consist of two distinct parts: the peduncle and the rachis. The peduncle is stout and muscular, and much of it is buried deep in the sand, anchoring the sea pen in place. The rachis is the part that bears the polyps, and genera such as *Virgularia* have fleshy leaves either side of the stem on which the polyps, are located. Members of this genus are normally found below a depth of about 20m (65ft) at the base of the reef slope, but other sea pens occur in shallow water. They feed on plankton, and many feed only at night. They are found throughout the region.

ANTHOZOANS – HEXACORALS

This subdivision of the anthozoans contains anemones, zoanthids, coralliomorphs and hard corals. They are called hexacorals because the polyp tentacles are arranged in multiples of six (rather than eight as in the octocorals).

ANEMONES

5 MAGNIFICENT SEA ANEMONE
Heteractis magnifica
This giant anemone from the Indo-Pacific has a smooth, brightly coloured column and blunt-ended tentacles. When fully open, the disk may be 1m (3ft) in diameter. It is found in open positions on the reef, attached to rock, and is one of ten species of giant anemone in the area. It is quite common in the region and widely distributed in the Indo-Pacific, playing host to 12 species of anemonefish over its range.

6 BULB TENTACLE ANEMONE
Entacmaea quadricolor
This is one of the most easily recognized of the giant anemones, due to the bulb-like expansion just below the tip of each tentacle. The column is always hidden in a crevice, and the anemone retracts rapidly if disturbed. It is found from the reef top to the base, and occurs throughout the region and wider Indo-Pacific. It is host to 13 species of anemonefish throughout its range.

1 Soft coral, bright pink form

2 Sea fan

3 Sea whip *(above left, left and above)*

4 Sea pen

5 Magnificent Sea Anemone

6 Bulb Tentacle Anemone

1 STINGING ANEMONE

Actinodendron sp.

These distinctive anemones grow up to about 30cm (1ft) in diameter, and have long tentacles, which usually have a knobbly appearance due to clusters of small finger-like vesicles. They are anchored in sand by the column, and can withdraw completely from view, leaving just a small depression. Some emerge only at night, and all tend to retract rapidly if disturbed. It catches plankton and small fish, and as the name implies, has a powerful sting. It occurs throughout the region.

2 TUBE-DWELLING ANEMONE

Cerianthus sp.

Cerianthids are actually more closely related to black corals than to anthozoan anemones. They are large, solitary anemones that live in soft but tough tubes, which they construct from specialized cells woven together with mucus. There are two rings of tentacles around the mouth. The outer ones are long and the inner ones much shorter, but both sets are narrow with trailing ends. Cerianthids are found in sheltered sandy or rubble patches, especially on the reef slope and in the entrance to caves. They feed on zooplankton but can also catch larger prey. They occur throughout the region.

ZOANTHIDS

Zoanthids are small, anemone-like cnidarians that may be solitary or colonial. They have two cycles of tentacles arranged in close-set rings around the margin of the oral disk. Some zoanthids contain toxins in the mucus and elsewhere in the body and should not be handled.

3 *PROTOPALYTHOA* sp.

There are several genera and numerous species of zoanthid, many of which have not been fully described. Most *Protopalythoa* species live in clusters of individual polyps that have long stems and a disk up to about 3cm (1⅛in) in diameter. They are low growing and sometimes form dense mats on the surface of the shallow reef and upper slope. Like other zoanthids, *Protopalythoa* can spread quite rapidly over the reef surface. It occurs throughout the region.

CORALLIMORPHARIANS

Corallimorpharians can be mistaken for other types of anemone, but are usually distinguished by the flattish oral disk, small protruding mouth and short tentacles that radiate out from the centre like the spokes of a wheel.

4 *AMPLEXIDISCUS FENESTRAFA*

This is the largest and most spectacular coralliomorph in the region, reaching a diameter of about 30cm (1ft) when fully expanded. Instead of capturing prey using stinging cells, it feeds by engulfing its prey. *Amplexidiscus* can close in 3 seconds, engulfing 4 litres (7 pints) of water in one go, and in this way it readily captures shrimps and fishes. As the disk is moved up and over, the mouth remains shut. Then when the edges of the disk have been drawn tightly together like a drawstring, the mouth is opened and the prey swallowed. It occurs fairly widely in shallow reef habitats. Clusters are quite common and are generally assumed to be a clone derived from the settlement of a single individual.

SCLERACTINIAN CORALS

Scleractinian (stony) corals are relatively easy to identify as a group, although they can be mistaken for 'rock' or confused with other reef dwellers that produce a calcium carbonate skeleton, such as fire coral and some of the red algae. Scleractinians have distinct patterns on the outside that relate to the arrangement of the coral polyps and skeleton; they are never smooth or featureless.

Identifying hard corals to species level can be difficult. Identification relies to a large extent on features of the skeleton, and often the distinguishing details are obscured by living tissue. At least 400 species of scleractinian coral belonging to around 70 genera occur in the region. Only a minute proportion can be illustrated here.

The living part of stony corals consists of polyps similar to those of anemones, with tentacles arranged in multiples of six. Each polyp produces a cup-like calcium carbonate skeleton (the corallite) around itself, and most stony corals are colonial, with hundreds or thousands of corallites joined together to form a solid structure (the corallum). Individual corallites range in size from about a millimetre to several

1 Stinging anemone *(right)*

2 Tube-dwelling anemone *(below)*

3 *Protopalythoa* sp. *(bottom left)*

4 *Amplexidiscus fenestrafa* *(bottom right)*

centimetres in diameter, and in some corals are quite easy to make out. In other species the corallite wall, instead of being a neat circular structure, may be elongate or meandering due to fusion of neighbouring corallites. It may form curious humps or even be missing altogether.

Corals capture food using stinging cells (nematocysts) on their tentacles. They also obtain a significant amount of nutrition from the thousands of single-celled plants (zooxanthellae) that live in the coral tissues. These cells pass on some of the organic matter they manufacture from carbon dioxide and sunlight.

Family Pocilloporidae

1 POCILLOPORA VERRUCOSA

Representatives of the family Pocilloporidae are common throughout the region. Most species have a branching growth form, but the branches range from extremely thin and delicate to broad and sturdy. *P. verrucosa* has intermediate-sized branches and is quite easy to recognize from the numerous small 'verrucae' on the surface, which are themselves covered in pinhead sized corallites. This species occurs mainly in shallow habitats where it forms small to medium-sized clumps that provide a home for many species of crustaceans and fish.

---

2 CORAL BLEACHING

Coral polyps, such as those of *Galaxea fascicularis*, are normally brownish due to the presence of zooxanthellae, but under stressful conditions they lose the algal cells, turn white and begin to starve. They can survive for weeks or even months without the microalgae, but their health deteriorates and they die unless the stress factor is removed. Factors such as ultraviolet radiation may be implicated in bleaching, but elevated temperatures caused by global warming are the main problem. Despite being tropical organisms, corals have a fairly narrow temperature tolerance. With a few exceptions, they flourish within the range 25–29°C (77–84°F), but bleach when the temperature is held above that for a few weeks by only one or two degrees Celsius.

Family Acroporidae

This family includes hundreds of species belonging to several genera. Corals of the genus *Acropora* often dominate in shallow areas, and are important reef-builders. The growth form of most species is branching and includes bottlebrush, staghorn, bush and table colonies. *Acropora* species have small, separate corallites, and in most species the polyps are retracted during the day. There are at least 80 species in the South-east Asian region.

3 ACROPORA HYACINTHUS

Table corals such as *A. hyacinthus* are widespread and successful colonists of shallow reef habitats in the region. They often reach several metres in diameter and the cave-like recesses at the base provide a safe retreat for various types of fish. Despite their rather delicate appearance, table corals can resist a surprising amount of water turbulence. When breakages occur, the entire colony usually snaps off at the stem. This does not necessarily mean their life is ended. Sometimes the colony slumps to one side and continues to grow. Upturned colonies can even sprout new branches from what was the undersurface.

4 ACROPORA AWI

This species is one of several recently described species of *Acropora* that appears to be restricted to the Indonesian side of the region. It has an upright, bottlebrush growth form and is pinkish-brown in colour. Colonies can be found along the reef rim and upper slope, a habitat that it shares with many other *Acropora* species.

5 MONTIPORA FOLIOSA

Montipora species have a wide range of growth forms. Some are branched, a few are massive, and many are encrusting or leafy, as illustrated by this colony of *M. foliosa*. They have extremely small corallites that are scarcely visible to the naked eye. Minute, usually white, flower-like polyps are often extended during the day, as they are in this photograph. The polyps are enclosed by narrow ridges which ornament the surface of the colony. *Montipora* species are abundant throughout the region.

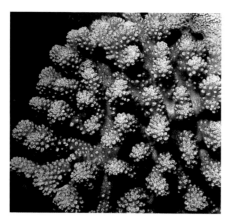
1 *Pocillopora verrucosa*

2 Coral bleaching of *Galaxea fascicularis*

3 *Acropora hyacinthus*

3 *Acropora hyacinthus* detail

4 *Acropora awi*

5 *Montipora foliosa*

Family Poritidae

This family includes several genera and many species. They all have a fairly light, porous skeleton, and small, crowded polyps with shared walls. Growth forms include crusts, mounds and branching colonies.

1 *PORITES LUTEA*

This is one of many species of *Porites* that occurs in the region. Heads 8m (26ft) in diameter occur on some reefs and are thought to be over 1,000 years old. Growth tends to be faster on the top with the result that a helmet-shaped colony is often formed. The recesses underneath make good hiding places for fish, and the sides and top of the colony are suitable attachment sites for reef organisms, such as featherstars, sponges and soft corals. Close examination of *Porites* reveals pin-head-sized corallites with joined walls that give the appearance of a miniature honeycomb.

2 *GONIOPORA LOBATA*

Goniopora species have long polyps and flower-like tentacles that are nearly always extended during the day. *G. lobata* forms thick columns, but these are obscured by the carpet of polyps, each of which is up to 10cm (4in) long. The mouth, which shows pink in the photograph, appears blue underwater. It occurs throughout the region.

Family Agariciidae

Agariciid corals come in a range of growth forms and are found in all reef habitats. Many are leafy; they have small corallites, often with joined walls.

3 *LEPTOSERIS GARDINERI*

This coral has a distinctive growth form and widely spaced corallites present only on the top surface of the 'leaves'. It is found throughout the region but is generally uncommon, except in certain localities. For example, on sheltered reef slopes it may form extensive tracts, covering many metres of reef. It is often only loosely attached.

Family Fungiidae

The most familiar members of this family are the mushroom corals. These are attached to the reef surface by a tiny stalk when very young, but then break away and become free-living. They may be extremely abundant in areas of coral, sand and rubble on reef slopes.

4 *SANDALOLITHA ROBUSTA*

S. robusta is a heavily built, dome-shaped, free-living coral. Unlike most *Fungia* species it has many small mouths rather than a single central one. It occurs throughout the region and the western Pacific and may be common on the upper reef slope. *Halomitra* is similar but is lightly built with small teeth on the septae.

Family Pectiniidae

5 *OXYPORA LACERA*

Pectiniid corals tend to form plate-like, encrusting or leafy colonies. This species is encrusting with thin, leafy edges. The corallites have a spikey appearance, protrude very slightly and are about 1cm (½in) in diameter. They generally have green or pink centres. It occurs throughout the region, and is particularly common on the reef slope and other deep reef habitats.

Family Mussidae

Corals in this family have large corallites, strong spines on the surface and a rather fleshy appearance. Polyps are retracted during the day.

6 *CYNARINA LACRYMALIS*

This solitary coral consists of a single, large, rounded corallite attached at its base. It does not usually exceed 8cm (3in) in diameter. A colourful, fleshy mantle covers the skeleton and is formed into bubble-like expansions over the septa. It is a relatively uncommon coral, which occurs throughout the region in sheltered areas and in deeper water on reef slopes.

7 *SYMPHYLLIA RECTA*

Symphyllia species form massive heads that are rounded, convex or flattened. The corallites are joined in longitudinal series to form a system of valleys and ridges, and the adjacent lateral walls are fused together. The distance across the wall in this species is about 12mm (½in), and as in other mussids, the surface of the coral is covered in fleshy tissue; the polyps are retracted during the day. This species occurs mainly along the reef rim and upper slope. It occurs throughout the region.

1 *Porites lutea*

2 *Goniopora lobata*

3 *Leptoseris gardineri*

4 *Sandalolitha robusta*

5 *Oxypora lacera*

6 *Cynarina lacrymalis*

7 *Symphyllia recta*

Family Faviidae

Faviid corals are well represented in all reef habitats. Colonies range from massive domes several metres in diameter to inconspicuous fist-sized growths. There are also some branching and laminar species. Corallites are separate in some species, but in others (the brain or meandrine corals) they are joined to form a system of walls and valleys.

1 ECHINOPORA LAMELLOSA

This coral is quite unusual for a faviid in consisting of leaves that form delicate scrolls. The corallites are distinct and about 3mm (⅛in) across. It may be common along the reef rim and upper slope of fairly sheltered reefs.

2 DIPLOASTREA HELIOPORA

Colonies of this coral are usually massive and rounded, but may be helmet-shaped in deeper water. The corallites are conspicuous and regular in appearance. They are closely packed and look like miniature truncated cones, the base of which is about 1cm (½in) in diameter. This coral is found on most reefs, especially on upper reef slopes or in areas exposed to swell or currents.

Family Euphyllidae

These corals used to be in the family Caryophylliidae, which includes the small, solitary 'cup corals'. Euphylliids are larger and colonial. Most have tentacles or vesicles that are extended during the day.

3 EUPHYLLIA ANCORA

This is a beautiful coral that can be seen occasionally on the reef rim and slope. It has prominent tentacles with anchor-shaped ends. The corallites are joined together in long series or meanders, and the whole colony may reach 50cm (1ft 8in) or more in diameter.

4 PLEROGYRA SINUOSA

Several species of Plerogyra occur in the region, and a feature of them all are the vesicles that are extended during the day. These retract at night, when feeding tentacles are extended. The shape of the vesicles in P. sinuosa is very variable: they may be big and balloon-like or more irregular, with small pointed protuberances. The skeleton underneath has very tall, leafy septa. This species is fairly common on reef slopes and in the shelter of boulders and coral heads.

Family Dendrophylliidae

Members of this family have fairly tall, cup-like corallites, and are solitary or colonial.

5 TUBASTRAEA MICRANTHA

Deep and shady habitats may have a well developed community of corals that lack zooxanthellae (ahermatypic species) and rely entirely on planktonic organisms for their nutrition. The largest of these forms is the tree coral T. micrantha, which forms tall, branching colonies. It is sometimes common on open slopes or terraces where there is fast current flow, generally below 15m (50ft). The green polyps are often extended during the day.

ANTHOZOANS – ANTIPATHARIA

There are many types of black coral. Some are very small with a highly divided, tangled mass of fine branches; others are bushy or form single stems. The common name 'black coral' refers to the hard, central supporting skeleton, which in some of the larger specimens is sometimes cut and polished to make jewellery.

6 BLACK CORAL BUSHES
Antipathes spp.

Black coral bushes may be found in shallow water where there are steep faces, but they are more typical of deep reefs and occur widely throughout the region. Colonies may be several metres tall and hundreds of years old. They provide a good refuge for small fish and many other animals.

7 WIRE CORAL
Cirrhipathes spiralis

Wire corals form a single, often coiled stem. They are usually greenish or yellow in colour and may be 1m (3ft) or more in height. Food is captured by the simple, unbranched polyp tentacles. They occur mainly on reef slopes with some current, and may be locally common. It is worth looking closely for tiny, well-disguised gobies *Bryaninops* spp., which live exclusively on wire coral. They usually occur in pairs and lay their eggs on a cleared section, which they then guard until hatching.

1 Echinopora lamellosa

2 Diploastrea heliopora

3 Euphyllia ancora

5 Tubastraea micrantha

4 Plerogyra sinuosa (above left)

6 Black corals: yellow bush (above middle) and white bush (above)

7 Wire coral (left)

WORMS

Many types of worm live on and around coral reefs, including flatworms, ribbonworms, peanut worms, echiurid worms, acorn worms and polychaete worms. Many are small or hidden from view and seldom noticed by divers. Those most frequently encountered are flatworms and various types of polychaete (segmented) worms.

FLATWORMS, PLATYHELMINTHES

1 *PSEUDOBICEROS BEDFORDI*

Flatworms are leaf-like and glide along the bottom using numerous tiny beating hairs on their undersides. Many species also have muscles, and the rippling effect of muscular waves passing along the body can be seen if they swim in open water. Flatworms feed on various small reef animals. The mouth is on the underside and the head end has simple eyes and two short antennae. *P. bedfordi* is one of many flatworms in the area. It reaches a length of about 8cm (3in) and is seen occasionally on reefs throughout the region.

POLYCHAETE WORMS

Polychaete worms (bristleworms and tubeworms) are abundant on reefs. The free-living and burrowing bristleworms tend to be secretive, but a range of tube-dwelling species can be seen. Some tubes are calcareous, while others are soft and pliable. Tube worms are sedentary, suspension feeders and have highly modified appendages on the head for collecting and sorting food.

2 CHRISTMAS TREE WORM

Spirobranchus giganteus

This tube worm has brightly coloured tentacles (red, blue, purple, yellow or green), which form two fan-shaped spiral whorls. When they are withdrawn, the tube can be plugged with a small calcareous plate. The tube is also calcareous, and the top end is visible when the tentacles retract. Live massive corals are the preferred habitat. Following a short planktonic stage, the larvae settle on live coral, probably finding an entry point where a polyp has died. The larvae do not actively burrow, but avoid being engulfed by continually adding new tube as the coral grows. This species is abundant on reefs throughout the tropics.

CRUSTACEANS

Crustaceans are incredibly numerous on coral reefs, but many are overlooked because of their small size and cryptic habits. Numerous species associate with other reef organisms, and a few are parasites. Typically, they have a segmented body with a calcareous outer skeleton. The legs and other appendages are jointed and modified, and used for a variety of purposes, including walking, swimming, defence, food capture, respiration and carrying eggs.

3 MANTIS SHRIMP

Odontodactylus scyllarus

Mantis shrimps are not true shrimps (order Decapoda), but belong to the Stomatopoda. They are unique crustaceans in that the front part of the head (bearing the eyes and antennules) moves independently from the rest. The stalked eyes can also be rotated independently of each other. The second pair of legs is adapted for the immobilization and capture of prey. They are normally folded up, but can be extended at incredible speed. Some seize and spear their prey; others like this species smash them with a fierce blow. Many species occur in the region, but they are generally quite shy and are often concealed in holes. The juveniles of *O. scyllarus* are yellowish, females greenish olive and males bright green with red marks on the appendages. They grow to about 18cm (7in) long and are found throughout the region, from shallow water to depths of 50m (165ft).

Worms/Crustaceans

1 *Pseudobiceros bedfordi (top)*   **2** Christmas Tree Worm *(above)*

3 Mantis shrimp

1 COMMENSAL SHRIMP

Periclimenes holthuisi on anemone

Numerous species of shrimp live in association with other reef animals, ranging from anemones to corals and echinoderms. In most cases the advantage appears to be only with the shrimp, which is protected or concealed by its host. Some of the commensals are perfectly camouflaged, but those in the genus *Periclimenes* are mainly transparent with colourful spots and stripes. There are many species and identification is difficult. *P. holthuisi* grows to a length of about 2.5cm (1in) and is a fairly common commensal on anemones throughout the region and wider Indo-Pacific.

2 BANDED BOXER SHRIMP

Stenopus hispidis

This species is one of a number that act as cleaners by picking external parasites and skin debris from their hosts. It has prominent red-and-white striped claws (chelae), and long white antennae, which are waved like flags to attract clients. Cleaning stations are close to the crevices, ledges and caves in which the shrimps live. Adult males and females live in pairs that may be stable for several years, and produce batches of eggs at regular intervals. Much of the cleaning is done at night. This species reaches a length of about 5cm (2in) and occurs throughout the tropics.

3 HERMIT CRAB

Dardanus megistos

Hermit crabs have a soft abdomen, which they protect by using empty mollusc shells as a home. *D. megistos* is a colourful hermit crab with a red body covered with black-edged white spots and spines. It is also one of the largest, growing to a length of about 15cm (6in). Like other hermits, it moves into progressively larger shells each time it moults. Large individuals are often found in the shells of the Giant Triton *Charonia tritonis*. Its food consists mainly of molluscs, which it can break open easily using its pincers. It is one of the commoner species, and occurs on reefs throughout the region and wider Indo-Pacific.

4 SLIPPER LOBSTER

Parrabacus antarcticus

Slipper lobsters are easily recognized by their extremely flattened carapace and appendages.

The antennae are reduced to thin, strong plates at the front of the body, and they have no pincers. The eyes are widely spaced. This species grows to about 20cm (8in) long. Like other slipper lobsters it hides in caves and holes during the day and emerges to feed at night, mostly on soft-bodied animals. It is found on reefs throughout the region and wider Indo-Pacific, from shallow water to depths of about 20m (50ft).

5 SMALL-DOT ANEMONE CRAB

Neopetrolisthes maculatus

This species is a porcelain crab and is more closely related to squat lobsters than true crabs – for example it has long antennae, and a tail that is tucked beneath the body. The small, closely set, reddish-brown dots are distinctive, and separate this species from the Large-dot Anemone Crab (*N. oshimai*), which has bigger, more widely spaced dots. Both species are found throughout the region, where they live in pairs amongst the tentacles or beneath the rim of sea anemones, particularly *Stichodactyla*. They gain protection from the anemone and use it as a base from which to forage. The first pair of walking legs are flattened and have large claws used for catching and handling prey.

6 SPIDER CRAB

Camposcia retusa

This small spider crab is common on reefs throughout the region, but it is incredibly well camouflaged and is often overlooked. It grows to only about 3cm (1in) in length, and the carapace and limbs are almost completely obscured by sponge, algae and pieces of debris that the crab picks up and puts in position. Sometimes its presence is revealed by the protruding black eyes. It occurs mainly on the shallow reef top, to depths of 15m (50ft), and forages for food at night.

7 *ETISUS DENTATUS*

Like many of the other decapod crabs that occur on reefs, *Etisus* is nocturnal. It is deep red in colour, robustly built and has large claws that can deal with shelled prey such as molluscs. It reaches a length of about 18cm (7in). Members of this genus occur throughout the region and wider Indo-Pacific, generally on the reef top and rim, to depths of about 15m (50ft).

1 Commensal shrimp *(left)*

2 Banded Boxer Shrimp *(above)*

3 Hermit crab *(above)*

4 Slipper lobster *(above left)*

5 Small-dot Anemone Crab *(left)*

6 Spider crab *(left)*

7 *Etisus dentatus (above)*

BRYOZOANS

1 Bryozoans occur widely on reefs, but are inconspicuous and often overlooked. The range of form and size of the colonies is often greater in shady places, such as caves, steep walls and the undersides of corals. Some are rigid, encrusting types (calcareous or soft), others, such as *Triphyllozoon*, form delicate fan-like structures. There may also be hanging tufts, resembling at first glance filamentous red algae. On close examination it is usually just possible to see a mosaic of tiny (1mm diameter) cubicles over the surface, which mark the position of each individual animal (zooid) making up the colony. Bryozoans are filter feeders, drawing water into the body using ciliated tentacles at the head end.

MOLLUSCS

Molluscs are a diverse group of thousands of species, and only a tiny selection is covered here. Their common features include a soft body with a covering called the mantle, a muscular foot, a tongue-like radula for feeding, gills for respiration and (in most species) an external, calcareous shell. Of the six main groups, only three are common on reefs: gastropods, bivalves and cephalopods. Many gastropods and bivalves have a cryptic lifestyle, which means they are hidden from view in nooks and crannies within the reef, or buried in sand. They are often small and quite a high proportion of the mobile species emerge only at night. Many lay eggs that are attached to the seabed, but there is also usually a planktonic phase.

GASTROPODS

Gastropods include snails with an external spiral shell (prosobranchs) and those that have either a reduced shell or no shell at all (opisthobranchs, including sea slugs).

2 WORM SNAIL
Dendropoma maxima
These curious animals are often not recognized as snails due to their highly modified structure. A calcareous shell is present, but it is uncoiled and largely hidden from view. In this species, the entrance to the shell is blocked by a horny plate on the snail's foot that acts as a lid (operculum). Other species lack the operculum, so the head end of the snail is visible. Worm snails are found buried in corals and rock on reefs throughout the region and wider Indo-Pacific. They feed by casting out strands of mucus, which trap plankton, and also use their gills to draw in currents of food-laden water. This species is often common, sometimes in high densities, on the shallow outer reef where water movement is strong. Eggs are brooded by the female and released as miniature adults, presumably so that they can colonize quickly and not be washed away to unsuitable terrain.

3 WENTLETRAP
Epitonium billeeanum
Wentletraps have small, highly ribbed shells and several species are known to feed on corals and anemones. *E. billeeanum* has a yellow or orange body and shell which perfectly matches the polyps of the dendrophylliid coral *Tubastraea* on which it feeds. The egg masses that are laid inside the corallites after the snail has eaten the polyp are similarly well disguised. Wentletraps occur throughout the region and wider Indo-Pacific, always associated with *Tubastraea*.

4 COWRIE
Cypraea (= Lyncina) lynx
Cowries have smooth, often brightly coloured shells with a slit-like aperture on the underside. This is produced as a result of the main shell whorl growing over and covering the central spire. *C. lynx* is one of many species of cowrie that occurs on and around reefs in the region. It grows to a length of about 4cm (1½in) and, when the mantle is extended, small polyp-like papillae are visible. These may help to disguise the animal as it hunts for food. It is found throughout the region and the wider Indo-Pacific. The pair in the photograph are laying eggs.

1 *Triphyllozoon inornatum*

2 Worm snail

3 Wentletrap

4 Cowrie

1 OVULID
Aclyvolva lanceolata

Ovulids are related to cowries, but have an egg or spindle-shaped shell. They live and feed on various soft corals, gorgonians and sponges, and are usually well camouflaged. *Aclyvolva lanceolata* has a red shell that closely mimics the gorgonian on which it lives, even down to the papillae on the mantle, which look just like polyps. It grows to a length of about 2.5cm (1in). It occurs throughout the region and wider Indo-Pacific, from shallow water to depths of about 20m (50ft), in association with gorgonians.

2 GIANT TRITON
Charonia tritonis

The Giant Triton is one of the largest of all gastropods and is instantly recognizable. This specimen is attacking a cushion star (*Culcita*), but it feeds on many other species of echinoderm, including the coral-feeding Crown-of-thorns starfish. It may grow to more than 50cm (1ft 8in) in length. It occurs on reefs throughout the region and wider Indo-Pacific, but is generally uncommon. It has been widely collected for the souvenir trade and is now protected in many countries.

3 THECACERA PACIFICA

This is one of several hundred species of nudibranch that occur in the region. Nudibranchs have no shell and are potentially a tasty snack for fish. However, many are distasteful and advertise this by their bright colours. Species belonging to the genus *Thecacera* have two pairs of appendages in addition to the sensory organs (rhinophores) at the front of the body, and the gills at the back. *T. pacifica* grows to a length of about 6cm (2¼in) and is found in fairly shallow water throughout the region, including seagrass beds. It is always worth looking out for egg masses in the vicinity of the adults. Nudibranchs are hermaphrodites, and get together to exchange sperm. After fertilization, eggs are deposited on a suitable surface. These will hatch into planktonic larvae that float in the water before settling back on the seabed.

4 PHYLLIDIA VARICOSA

There are many species of *Phyllidia* in the area, all of which have knobbly protuberances on the body. Most are brightly coloured and a potential meal for predators but, when disturbed, *P. varicosa* produces mucus that is toxic to fish. The toxin involved actually comes from the sponge on which the nudibranch feeds. It recycles it, using it as a protective constituent of its body mucus. This species is common throughout the region and wider Indo-Pacific.

BIVALVES

Bivalves have a soft body enclosed within two hinged shell valves. There are numerous species associated with reef habitats. Many are buried in sand and cannot be seen; others are partly or completely embedded in reef limestone or in corals, with parts visible. Bivalves obtain their food by drawing in water over internal gills and extracting planktonic food and nutritious particles.

5 PEDUM SPONDYLOIDEUM

Scallops settle preferentially on corals at the end of their larval phase. As they grow, they inhibit the development of the coral around them with the result that they end up in a crevice. The only part of the adult that is visible is the brightly coloured mantle and the outer edges of the shell. The eyespots on the margin of the mantle are sensitive to light and the shell valves close rapidly if a shadow passes over. This species is widely distributed in the Indo-Pacific.

6 GIANT CLAM
Tridacna gigas

This is by far the largest of the seven species of giant clam that occur in the area, and grows to a length of over 130cm (4ft 4in). The shell is distinctly ribbed, but there is no sculpturing in the form of flutes. The mantle is usually brown with iridescent blue-green circles. Like other giant clams, *T. gigas* feeds by filtering seawater over its gills and removing plankton and other food particles. It supplements this with organic matter synthesized by the population of symbiotic algae (zooxanthellae) that live in the mantle tissues. *T. gigas* occurs throughout the region but has been drastically over-exploited and tends to be seen only in protected areas.

1 Ovulid

2 Giant Triton

3 *Thecacera pacifica (above)*, laying eggs *(right)*

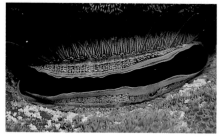

4 *Phyllidia varicosa*

5 *Pedum spondyloideum*

6 Giant clam

CEPHALOPODS

Cephalopods (octopus, squid and cuttlefish) are advanced and intelligent molluscs, with well-developed eyes and complex behaviour patterns. The shell is generally internal, and the head has prominent tentacles. Octopus are common on reefs and live mainly on the bottom, hiding in holes and searching out prey, such as crabs. They have eight arms, well supplied with large suckers.

1 REEF CUTTLEFISH
Sepia latimanus

Cuttlefish have ten arms with suction disks on their inner surface. This is one of the largest species, reaching 50cm (1ft 8in) in length. It may be found singly or in pairs, and with care can be approached quite closely. Colour patterns are remarkably variable and change in an instant, depending on mood and habitat. It is quite common throughout the region, especially on reef slopes.

ECHINODERMS

Echinoderms occur only in the marine environment. They have an internal skeleton of small calcareous plates, and a water vascular system consisting of fluid-filled canals. Tiny tube feet are a part of this system and are used for locomotion and capturing food.

CRINOIDS, FEATHERSTARS

Most of the reef species have 10–20 feathery arms, sometimes more. There are also short, segmented 'cirri' on the underside that are used for movement and anchorage. Numerous species occur in the area but identification is often difficult.

2 OXYCOMANTHUS BENNETTI

This is one of the most frequently seen species of crinoid in the region, partly because it is active both by day and night. It secures the best feeding position by clinging to protruding rocks or reef animals, and sometimes occurs in groups. It has as many as 100 arms and comes in at least four colour varieties.

3 COMANTHINA sp.

Like other featherstars, *Comanthina* is a suspension feeder, capturing small particles on its arm pinnules. The food is then rolled in mucus and propelled down to the mouth which, unlike other echinoderms, faces upwards. Crinoids rely on supplies of food being swept past, and so are found in areas of moderate to strong current.

ASTEROIDS, STARFISH

Like other echinoderms, starfish typically have a five-sided symmetry, as exemplified by the five arms seen in most species. The mouth and innumerable sucker-like tube feet are on the underside. Food varies from detritus to sponges, seasquirts and shelled molluscs.

4 NARDOA FRIANTI

Nardoa species can be distinguished by the warty protuberances on the upper surface. These are particularly prominent in *N. frianti*, a colourful species seen occasionally on reefs throughout the region, from a few metres depth to over 40m (130ft). It grows to about 14cm (5½in) in diameter.

5 PROTOREASTER NODOSUS

This starfish is easily recognized by its heavy build and the blunt, black spines set against a pinkish body. *P. lincki* is similar but has a grey body with sharper, bright red spines. *P. nodosus* may be abundant in sandy habitats, both in shallow water and at the base of the reef.

6 LINCKIA LAEVIGATA

This starfish, widespread throughout the region, is usually blue, but may also be pale brownish. It is a large species with a diameter up to 40cm (1ft 6in). It is particularly common in shallow water, but is found as deep as 50m (165ft). It feeds on coralline algae, micro-organisms and detritus, which it 'mops-up' from the reef surface.

1 Reef Cuttlefish

2 *Oxycomanthus bennetti*

3 *Comanthina* sp. *(left)*

4 *Nardoa frianti (above)*

5 *Protoreaster nodosus (left)*

6 *Linckia laevigata (above)*

1 *CULCITA NOVAEGUINEAE*

Young cushionstars have recognizable arms, but as they grow the arms disappear. Their maximum size is about 25cm (10in) across. The colour is variable, ranging from orange-red to dark green. Like other echinoderms, it has commensal organisms living with it. Close examination will usually reveal the small shrimp *Periclemenes soror* on the underside. It is found in most reef habitats, where it feeds mainly on corals.

2 CROWN-OF-THORNS
Acanthaster planci

This starfish reaches 60cm (2ft) in diameter, has up to 23 arms and is covered with strong, sharp spines. It matures at 2–3 years of age, and each female produces up to 100 million eggs in a single spawning season. The larvae drift and feed on microscopic algae before settling on the bottom. For at least the first 6 months, the young starfish feed on coralline algae, but then they switch their attention to live coral, preferring branching species such as *Acropora*. It occurs widely in the Indo-Pacific, and its 'normal' density is quite low. However, plagues sometimes occur, causing extensive coral mortality.

OPHIUROIDS, BRITTLESTARS AND BASKETSTARS

3 *OPHIOTHRIX* sp.

Brittlestars have a small central body with long, slender arms. These may be deliberately shed if the animal is disturbed or attacked, and replacements can be grown. The arms are highly flexible and allow rapid movement, while the tube feet are reduced to small, tentacle-like structures used for capturing particles of food. Some brittlestars catch planktonic food, while others pick up detritus from the reef surface. Many brittlestars live in association with sponges, fire coral and gorgonians, while others live under rocks and rubble, emerging to feed at night. This is a widespread species found throughout the Indo-Pacific.

4 BASKETSTAR
Astroboa nuda

The basketstar is a specialized brittlestar with thin, highly divided arms adapted for filter feeding.

During the day, basketstars curl into a tight ball and hide beneath corals and in crevices. At night they emerge, unfurl their arms and start feeding (torchlight makes them recoil). The fine arm branches sweep from side to side, seizing plankton. As daylight approaches, the basketstar retreats, and in the safety of the reef, food is transferred to the mouth. The basketstar occurs on reefs throughout the region.

ECHINOIDS, SEA URCHINS

Sea urchins have a body enclosed in a shell consisting of closely fitting, calcium carbonate plates. This is armed with numerous spines, which are often toxic. The spines are attached by a type of ball-and-socket joint and are highly mobile. Along with the tube feet, they help the urchin to move, as well as defend it from predators.

5 LONG-SPINED URCHIN
Diadema setosum

Of the species of long-spined sea urchins in the area, *D. setosum* has the longest, thinnest spines, and has a bright red or orange ring around the anal opening on the top of the test. The outside of the spines is coated with poisonous mucus, which causes considerable discomfort if the spines penetrate the skin. Long-spined urchins usually aggregate in shady crevices and holes during the day, emerging at night to graze on algae. This species is abundant to common throughout the region, especially in shallow sand and rubble areas.

6 FIRE URCHIN
Asthenosoma varium

This species has a flexible rather than rigid test, and sharp spines with globular swellings (sacs) just below the tips. The small white sacs are formed from the thin layer of skin that covers the spines. They contain a virulent poison, which is released if the spines are broken or pierce the flesh of an attacker. Despite their spines, sea urchins are vulnerable to day-active predators, such as triggerfish. Although some are visible during the day, others remain hidden inside holes and crevices, only emerging to graze under the safety of darkness. Despite being highly venomous, the Fire Urchin is only active at night. It is found throughout the region, mainly in sand and rubble habitats.

1 *Culcita novaeguineae (left)*

2 Crown-of-thorns

3 *Ophiothrix* sp. on gorgonian
(left)

4 Basketstar *(above)*

5 Long-spined urchin
(below left)

6 Fire Urchin
(below)

HOLOTHURIANS, SEA CUCUMBERS

Sea cucumbers are bilaterally rather than radially symmetrical echinoderms. The body is elongated with a distinct front and rear end. Tube feet are best developed on the underside, and these are used in locomotion. Those around the head are generally larger and are adapted for food capture. Sea cucumbers are found in many reef habitats, where they feed either on organic detritus or plankton.

1 SYNAPTULA LAMPERTI

This small sea cucumber grows to about 5cm (2in), and has a soft, worm-like body without tube feet. The red longitudinal stripes against an opaque white background distinguishes it from other synaptulids. *S. lamperti* lives on the surface of large sponges where it is thought to be protected from predators by the toxicity of its host. In turn, the sea cucumbers may provide a service by feeding on detritus that settles on the sponge, so helping to prevent the inhalant pores from becoming clogged. It is found in South-east Asia and Australia.

2 THELENOTA ANANAS

This is an example of one of the many species that feeds by ingesting sand and sediment and removing the nutritious elements, leaving a trail of sandy faeces in its wake. *T. ananas* reaches a length of about 50cm (1ft 8in) and has a distinctive 'armour' of pointed tubercles covering its leathery skin. Known as 'bêche-de-mer' it is considered a delicacy in many parts of the Indo-Pacific and has been over-exploited in some areas. It is found in rubble or sandy areas of the reef front, and feeds on organic detritus. It is widespread throughout the Indo-Pacific.

ASCIDIANS

Ascidians (sea squirts) do not look like particularly advanced animals, yet they are considered relatively advanced because they are closely related to vertebrates. The tail of the tiny planktonic larva is strengthened with a rod-like structure very similar to the vertebrate backbone, and the gullet (pharynx) of the adult is perforated like the gills of fish to form a filtering device called the branchial sac.

3 CLAVELINA ROBUSTA

This striking species of ascidian consists of tightly packed clusters of tall zooids, each about 2cm (¾in) tall. The siphons are ringed in white, yellow or green while the rest of the body is dark blue to black. Like other ascidians, *C. robusta* feeds on planktonic organisms, drawing water in through the larger oral siphon at the top, passing it through the branchial sac, and then out of the cloacal siphon. It is found on reefs throughout the region.

4 DIDEMNUM MOLLE

This species consists of many zooids, individually about 3cm (1¼in) tall, that are joined together to form a rounded colony. There is a single large outgoing (cloacal) aperture, and many very small oral siphons. The latter are visible as dots spread closely over the surface of the animal. The green colour of *D. molle* is due to the presence of symbiotic algae (*Prochloron*), which live within the tissues. This species is one of the most commonly seen colonial ascidians, and occurs widely on reefs throughout the region and the wider Indo-Pacific.

5 POLYCARPA AURATA

This is one of the larger ascidians, growing to a height of about 10cm (4in). It may be solitary, but often is found in small groups. *P. aurata* is easily recognized by the mottled yellow and blue coloration. It is one of the most conspicuous and widely distributed ascidians, occurring in a wide range of habitats.

1 *Synaptula lamperti*

2 *Thelenota ananas*

3 *Clavelina robusta*

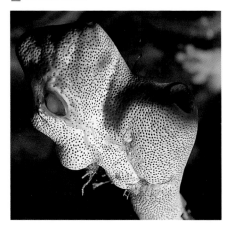

4 *Didemnum molle*

5 *Polycarpa aurata*

CARTILAGINOUS FISH
Class Chondrichthyes

Sharks and rays (elasmobranchs) are distinguished by having a cartilaginous rather than a bony skeleton, multiple (5–7) gill slits rather than a single one, and small non-overlapping scales. These are called dermal denticles ('skin teeth') and give the skin its characteristic sandpaper texture. The teeth in the jaw are modified dermal denticles and are replaced throughout the fish's life. Elasmobranchs practise internal fertilization, and the male can be identified by his claspers (modified pelvic fins), which look a bit like a penis. The embryo is usually retained within the female's body until it is born as a fully-developed, independent fish, but some embryos are 'laid' in egg cases and develop externally, drawing on yolk reserves in the cases.

SHARKS

Sharks eat living animals, varying in size from zooplankton to molluscs, fish and turtles, and their senses are very well developed to locate their prey. Many are more active at night and have a reflective device in their eyes, which increases sensitivity in dim light. They can detect low frequency vibrations occurring a considerable distance away with the lateral line system, a sense organ unique to fish that runs along each side of the body. It consists of a row of tiny holes that connect with fluid-filled canals that house the sense cells. The sense of smell in sharks is also well developed. In addition, they are also able to detect low-level electric fields, such as that emitted by the muscular activity of other animals. As many as 50 species of shark may occur in the area.

WHALE SHARK,
FAMILY RHINCODONTIDAE

 WHALE SHARK
Rhincodon typus

The Whale Shark is the largest fish in the world, generally reaching a length of about 12m (39ft), but sometimes several metres longer. It is easily recognized by the spots on the dorsal surface, white belly and wide, tooth-less mouth. Food consists of zooplankton, small fish, squid and small pelagic fish that are trapped in spongy tissues that hang between the gill arches. Large individuals tend to be solitary, but the smaller ones may move around in groups. *Ecology:* It occurs in all tropical areas, and may occasionally be seen around reefs. It may migrate considerable distances in search of food.

ZEBRA SHARKS,
FAMILY STEGOSTOMIDAE

 LEOPARD SHARK
Stegostoma fasciatum

The family name zebra shark is from the appearance of the juvenile, which is dark with many pale stripes. In contrast, the adult is pale with dark spots. It commonly reaches a length of about 2.3m (7½ft), but may grow to 3.5m (11½ft). Like several other bottom-dwelling sharks (e.g. nurse sharks and bamboo sharks) it is harmless and slow-moving, has barbels on the nose, a relatively small mouth and a poorly developed lower tail lobe. *Ecology:* It occurs throughout the region from shallow water to depths of over 40m (130ft). It is generally found out in the open, on sand and rubble patches, spending much of its time resting on the bottom.

1 Whale Shark

2 Leopard Shark

REQUIEM OR WHALER SHARKS, FAMILY CARCHARINIDAE

All species of the genus *Carcharinus* have sleek bodies and two dorsal fins of unequal size. The first is larger and situated above the ventral fin while the second is much smaller. The upper lobe of the tail fin is much larger than the lower one. At least 20 species may be encountered in the region. Several are potentially dangerous, especially if spearfishing is going on nearby or if they are excited or aggravated by being fed by divers.

1 BLACKTIP REEF SHARK

Carcharinus melanopterus

This Blacktip Reef Shark as its name suggests has black tips to the fins, although these may fade with age. There is a white stripe along the side of its silvery body. It grows to a length of 2.5m (8ft). *Ecology:* It occurs in warm waters around the globe. Juveniles may be seen off beaches while adults are primarily open-water hunters, but sometimes visit reefs when following prey such as mackerel.

RAYS

Rays are distinguished by the expanded, wing-like pectoral fins, which are attached to the fish's head. The gill slits are on the underside of the body and water passes over them after it has been drawn in through a small hole (spiracle) behind each eye.

STINGRAYS, FAMILY DASYATIDAE

Stingrays have a long tail with one or two long, venomous spines near the base. These spines are used for defence but are seldom a hazard for divers. The main danger is for people wading with bare feet in shallow areas. A sting ray's reaction when trodden on is to lash its tail up and forward, impaling the foot before it can be lifted away. Rapid treatment with hot water is the best way of treating the wound, as it denatures the poison. About ten species of stingray occur in the region.

2 BLUE-SPOTTED RIBBONTAIL RAY

Taeniura lymma

This species is easily recognized by its rounded shape and distinct blue spots. It reaches a length of about 2.4m (8ft) and a width of over 90cm (3ft) across the 'wings'. *Ecology:* It occurs throughout the region on sandy patches or beneath ledges or overhangs, from shallow water to depths of 40m (130ft) or more.

3 BLUE-SPOTTED STINGRAY

Dasyatis kuhlii

The spots on this species are less distinct than in the Blue-spotted Ribbontail Ray, and the body is angular (kite-shaped). It reaches a length of about 80cm (2½ft) and has a 'wingspan' of about 40cm (1ft 4in). *Ecology:* It occurs in shallow sandy areas adjacent to reefs and is found throughout the region. It usually lies on the bottom covered in sand, with just the eyes and spiracles visible. Feeding is mostly at dusk and dawn and often pits can be seen in the sand where molluscs have been hunted out.

EAGLE RAYS, FAMILY MYLIOBATIDAE

Eagle rays have triangular 'wings' with a narrow head protruding from the front of the body (contrast manta rays). The tail is long with one or more venomous spines at the base in most species.

4 SPOTTED EAGLE RAY

Aetobatus narinari

This species can be distinguished from other eagle rays that occur in the region by the pattern of white spots on the dorsal surface. The 'wings' are up to about 2.4m (8ft) across. *Ecology:* It occurs in tropical waters around the globe and may be seen cruising in open water around the reef. It feeds on large, attached shells, such as oysters and clams, and may also dig for sand-dwelling crustaceans and molluscs, using its plate-like teeth to crush the shells.

1 Blacktip Reef Shark

2 Blue-spotted Ribbontail Ray

3 Blue-spotted Stingray

4 Spotted Eagle Ray

MANTA RAYS, FAMILY MOBULIDAE

Mantas have large, triangular 'wings' and a wide mouth flanked by two horn-like flaps (cephalic flaps). The tail is long and thin, and the spines are either extremely small, or completely lacking.

1 MANTA RAY
Manta birostris

This ray grows to a huge size, with a maximum 'wingspan' of around 6.7m (22ft), and has

very well-developed head flaps. The dorsal surface of the manta is darkish with pale markings. *Mobula* rays are smaller and have less well-developed head flaps. *Ecology:* The Manta Ray occurs in warm waters around the globe and is an occasional visitor to plankton-rich areas of the reef. When feeding it unrolls the two flaps on the front of the head to direct a stream of plankton-laden water into the mouth. Mantas often come to cleaning stations on the reef, and if divers are unobtrusive these magnificent fish can be observed at close quarters.

MORAY EELS
Family Muraenidae

Moray eels are elongate fish with continuous dorsal and anal fins that join up with the tail fin. They have no pectoral fins. Over 30 species of moray occur on reefs in the region, but they are often hidden in holes during the day. They have sharply pointed canine teeth, suited to their fish-eating habits; they hunt mostly at night. The constant opening and closing of the mouth seen in many species is not a sign of imminent attack, but merely an action that pumps water over the gills for respiration.

2 STARRY OR SNOWFLAKE MORAY
Echidna nebulosa

All *Echidna* species have a blunter, more rounded head than other morays. The Starry Moray is easily identified by its whitish body and the series of dark spots with pale centres that run down its side. It reaches a length of about 70cm (2ft 4in). *Ecology:* It occurs throughout the region, especially in shallow parts of the reef. It may even leave the water to move from one tide pool to another. Its food consists mainly of crustaceans.

3 YELLOW-MARGINED OR LEOPARD MORAY
Gymnothorax flavimarginatus

This species has a yellowish-brown body covered with small, irregular dark spots. There is a larger black mark at the gill opening. This is one of the

largest morays, reaching a maximum length of about 3m (10ft). It may be confused with the Giant Moray (*G. javanicus*), which also occurs in the area, but the latter is browner and has characteristic dark markings reminiscent of leopard's spots. *Ecology:* It occurs throughout the region, and throughout the Indo-Pacific, mainly in holes and crevices on offshore reefs, from shallow water to depths of at least 150m (500ft). It hunts for fish and crustaceans at night.

4 WHITEMOUTHED MORAY
Gymnothorax meleagris

As indicated by its common name, a distinctive feature of this species is the white inside of the mouth. It also has small white spots on the body, which may join up with one another. It reaches a length of about 1.2m (4ft). *Ecology:* It is seen occasionally on reefs throughout the region and also in the wider Indo-Pacific, from shallow water to depths of over 36m (120ft).

2 Starry Moray

1 Manta Ray

3 Yellow-margined Moray

4 Whitemouthed Moray

SNAKE EELS
Family Ophichthidae

This group gets its common name from the thin, round body, which is snake-like in appearance. Most species have a pointed nose and tubular nostrils that point downwards. Probably over 20 species occur in the area, but they tend to be fairly secretive, hiding in dark holes or in sand during the day, sometimes with just their heads visible. At night they become more active, possibly to coincide with the emergence of small prey organisms from the sand around their burrows. A few species leave their burrows and holes to forage elsewhere.

BANDED SNAKE EEL
Myrichthys colubrinus

This species is sometimes mistaken for a sea snake because of its black bands, but it is readily distinguished by the lack of scales and the presence of small fins. The Saddled Snake Eel (*Leiuranus simicinctus*) also has black bars, but these do not reach all the way around the body. The Banded Snake Eel reaches a length of about 1.9m (6ft). *Ecology:* It occurs throughout the region and the wider Indo-Pacific, mainly in shallow sandy habitats. It feeds on fish and crustaceans.

SPOTTED SNAKE EEL
Myrichthys maculosus

When fully grown, this species has a row of large black spots down the side, but younger fish have smaller, more numerous spots. It reaches a length of about 1m (3ft). *Ecology:* It occurs in sandy areas on reefs throughout the region and the wider Indo-Pacific, from shallow water to depths of over 250m (820ft). These elusive fish burrow using their pointed snouts, but they are equally adept at retreating tail-first into the sand.

GARDEN EELS
Family Congridae

Garden eels are easily distinguished from other types of eel by the thin, round body, and the presence of small pectoral fins. They live in large colonies at certain current-swept sites, often on sand plains at mid-depth, for example on sandy terraces, or on deeper slopes. The eels construct individual sandy burrows, which they seldom leave. When feeding, they extend the front part of the body but leave about two-thirds in the burrow.

SPOTTED GARDEN EEL
Heteroconger hassi

This species has small, closely set spots and two large black ones towards the front end of the body. It grows to a length of about 50cm (1ft 8in). *Ecology:* This species occurs throughout the region, from depths of about 6–40m (20–130ft). The body, seldom thicker than a finger, projects from the sand and is moved in a graceful, wave-like movement as the fish search out and snap up plankton. They stay in their burrows even when spawning, which they do by stretching over to a mate nearby and entwining bodies. Garden eels are very sensitive to the presence of divers and retreat rapidly into their burrows even at the most cautious approach.

1 Banded Snake Eel

2 Spotted Snake Eel

3 Spotted Garden Eel

CATFISH
Family Plotosidae

Catfish occur mainly in fresh water, but a few are marine. They have an elongate body with the dorsal and anal fins continuous with the tail fin. There is a cluster of barbels around the mouth, which have a sensory function. The first dorsal and pectoral spines are extremely venomous – even a juvenile can deliver a painful sting. Catfish are similar in appearance to cusk eels (Ophididae), but the pelvic fins on the latter are very small and situated far forward, almost under the eye.

1 STRIPED CATFISH
Plotosus lineatus

Of the few catfish likely to be seen in the region, this is the commonest, and is easily recognized by the white stripes along the body. It reaches a

length of about 30cm (1ft). *Ecology:* It occurs throughout the region and the wider Indo-Pacific on coastal reefs and seagrass beds from shallow water to depths of over 30m (100ft). Adults are solitary and hide under ledges during the day, but juveniles gather in groups of hundreds of tightly packed individuals that move in unison.

LIZARDFISH
Family Synodontidae

Lizardfish have rounded, elongate bodies with a short, high dorsal fin and a tiny fleshy one further back. The mouth is large, with a wide gape, and is packed with sharp teeth, including some on the tongue. About eight species occur in the region.

2 GREYSTREAK LIZARDFISH
Synodus dermatogenys

Like other species of lizardfish, the Greystreak is mottled, with ill-defined brownish bars. It can usually be distinguished by the greyish streak along

the side of the body, and its habit of burying itself in sand with only eyes and nostrils showing. It reaches a length of about 18cm (7in). *Ecology:* It occurs on sandy reef areas throughout the region from shallow water to depths of over 20m (50ft). It lies buried in sand in wait for small fish and shrimps, which it pounces on with great speed.

CLINGFISH
Family Gobiesocidae

Clingfish are tiny and many species have the pelvic fins fused to form a suction disk. The head is flattened and the body has a thick layer of mucus covering the scaleless skin.

3 FEATHERSTAR CLINGFISH
Discotrema sp.

Several similar species of *Discotrema* occur in the area. They are small fish, generally less than

4mm in length. *Ecology: Discotrema* species occur throughout the Indo-Pacific in association with featherstars (crinoids). They remain hidden amongst the arms of the featherstar and are well disguised.

1 Striped Catfish

2 Greystreak Lizardfish

3 Featherstar Clingfish

FROGFISH
Family Batrachoididae

Frogfish (sometimes called toadfish) are elongate, with a large head and mouth and big eyes in a frog-like position on the top of the head. Several species occur in the region, but most are associated with mixed ground around reefs, rather than reefs themselves.

BANDED FROGFISH
Halophyrne diemensis

The main distinguishing feature of the Banded Frogfish is that the gill slit extends only about half the length of the pectoral fin base, whereas in the other species it runs the whole length. It reaches a length of about 26cm (10in). *Ecology:* It occurs on reefs throughout the region and also in the eastern Indian Ocean and northern Australia. It often hides in crevices and holes.

ANGLERFISH
Family Antennariidae

Anglerfish (confusingly also sometimes called frogfish) have a bulbous body with a large, upturned mouth. The pectoral fins are jointed and used for 'walking' on the seabed, and the first dorsal fin is modified to form a 'fishing rod' (illicium) with a lure at its tip. This apparatus is jiggled around to attract other fish, which are then snapped up and eaten whole. Anglerfish have loose, flabby skin and the body can distend to accommodate prey larger than themselves. Mature females lay a mass of eggs on the seabed every few days. At least eight species of anglerfish occur in the area, but they are well camouflaged and often overlooked.

PAINTED ANGLERFISH
Antennarius pictus

The skin of this species has few if any warty protuberances and the illicium is long and marked with numerous dark cross bands. The body colour varies from plain yellow to brownish, and it often has dark spots ringed in white. It reaches a length of about 16cm (6in). *Ecology:* It occurs on reefs throughout the region and the wider Indo-Pacific.

GARFISH or HALFBEAKS
Family Hemiramphidae

    Garfish are silvery, elongate fish that are easily recognized by the unequal-sized jaws: the lower one is long and thin, while the upper one is short. This distinguishes them from needlefish (Family Belonidae), which have a similar body shape, but have needle-like jaws of equal length. Garfish occur in schools at the surface of the water above reefs. They have a mixed diet of zooplankton, small fish and algae. Several species occur in the area, but they lack distinctive markings and are not easy to identify.

1 Banded Frogfish

2 Painted Anglerfish

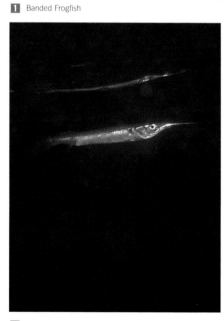

3 Garfish, *Hyporhamphus dussumieri*

SOLDIERFISH AND SQUIRRELFISH
Family Holocentridae

These are medium-sized, deep-bodied fish with large eyes and stout spines on the fins. They are mainly red in colour. Squirrelfish are distinguished from soldierfish by the presence of a large spine on the cheek. All members of this family rest during the day in or around caves, underhangs, crevices and amongst corals. At night they become active and disperse in search of food. Soldierfish feed mostly on zooplankton, while squirrelfish forage over rubble, sand and seagrass for invertebrates and small fish, such as cardinalfish. There are up to 30 species in the region.

 BLACKFIN SOLDIERFISH
Myripristis adusta

Soldierfish are often difficult to distinguish from one another, but the Blackfin Soldierfish is fairly easily identified by its bronze colour and the dark marking along the outer margins of the fins. It reaches over 30cm (1ft) in length. *Ecology:* It occurs on reefs throughout region and in the wider Indo-Pacific, from shallow water to depths of over 25m (80ft).

2 SPINY SQUIRRELFISH
Sargocentron spiniferum

This squirrelfish is easily recognized by its large size, protruding mouth and the very long spine on the gill cover. It grows to a length of about 45cm (1ft 6in). *Ecology:* It occurs on reefs throughout the region and in the wider Indo-Pacific, from shallow water to depths of over 120m (400ft).

3 SMALLMOUTH SQUIRRELFISH
Sargocentron microstoma

Like a number of other squirrelfish, this species has white and red stripes on its body and a red margin on the dorsal fin. It is distinguished by its slender body and the very long third spine on the anal fin. Its maximum length is about 20cm (8in). *Ecology:* It occurs on reefs throughout the region and also in the Pacific Ocean and central Indian Ocean. It lives in all reef habitats, from shallow water to depths of over 180m (600ft).

TRUMPETFISH
Family Aulostomidae

There is only a single genus in this family, and two species: one in the Indo-Pacific and one in the Atlantic. Trumpetfish have an elongate body with a long, trumpet-shaped snout and small tail fin. They have similarities with the flutemouth (*see* page 68) and some authors include the Indo-Pacific species in the Family Fistularidae and name it the Painted Flutemouth.

4 TRUMPETFISH
Aulostoma chinensis

This species reaches a length of about 80cm (2ft 7in) and exhibits a range of colour phases and patterns, from bright yellow to pale grey or brown with vertical bars or narrow longitudinal bands. *Ecology:* It is common on reefs through-out the region, from shallow water to depths of over 120m (400ft). Trumpetfish have a very extensible mouth and use suction to capture prey, such as small fish and crustaceans. They are not agile swimmers and use stealth to make a close approach. They sometimes mingle with schools of herbivorous fish and may shadow larger fish, such as rockcod, ready to dart at small prey, or even steal food from their 'host'.

1 Blackfin Soldierfish

2 Spiny Squirrelfish

3 Smallmouth Squirrelfish

4 Trumpetfish

FLUTEMOUTH
Family Fistularidae

Flutemouths are distinguished from trumpetfish by their long, narrow snout and the very long filament on the tail. This is formed from the elongated middle pair of rays on the tail fin.

1 SMOOTH FLUTEMOUTH
Fistularia commersonii

The Smooth Flutemouth is bluish in colour and reaches a length of about 1.5m (5ft). At night it changes colour to display a series of broad dark bands on a pale background. The only other species likely to be seen is the Rough

Flutemouth (*Fistularia petimba*), which has a brownish body with a row of bony plates along its side. *Ecology:* Juveniles may enter estuaries, while older fish are found in sandy and reef areas throughout the region, from shallow water to depths of over 130m (425ft). Individuals normally move around in small groups, a few metres above the seabed. They feed mainly on small fish.

RAZORFISH
Family Centriscidae

Members of this family have a narrow, elongate body and are easily identified by their habit of swimming upright, with the head down.

2 GROOVED RAZORFISH or SHRIMPFISH
Centriscus scutatus

This is the only species of razorfish to occur in the region. It has a long, thin, pointed snout and a narrow body covered in bony plates. The dor-

sal, caudal and anal fins are in a cluster at the tail end of the fish, but always point upwards because razorfish swim in a head-down posture. It reaches a maximum length of about 15cm (6in). *Ecology:* It occurs on reefs throughout the region and in the wider Indo-Pacific. It shelters between the spines of long-spined sea urchins or in branching corals, and feeds on plankton.

GHOST PIPEFISH
Family Solenostomidae

Members of this family are closely related to the true pipefishes.

3 HARLEQUIN GHOST PIPEFISH
Solenostomus paradoxus

This unmistakable fish has a long snout, thin body and large fins. It grows to a length of about 16cm (6¼in). The intricate pattern of reddish spots and stripes and presence of numerous skin flaps on the body distinguish it from *S.*

cyanopterus, the other species of ghost pipefish that occurs in the region. *Ecology:* An uncommon species, occurring on sheltered inshore reefs and seagrass beds throughout the region, and the wider Indo-Pacific. It may swim head-down, often amongst seagrasses, seaweeds, gorgonians or similar shelter. Its food consists of plankton and small invertebrates.

1 Smooth Flutemouth

2 Grooved Razorfish *(below)*

3 Harlequin Ghost Pipefish

SEAHORSES AND PIPEFISH
Family Syngnathidae

These fish have a protruding snout and a body encased in bony rings. Pipefish are very elongate and the head is on the same axis as the body, but seahorses swim upright and the head is flexed at an angle to the body so that it points forwards. The tail in seahorses is also distinctive because it is curled and prehensile. There are numerous species in the family, but many are small, live in holes, or are well camouflaged and so are easily overlooked. They live in pairs, and when breeding the female deposits her eggs in her partner's brood pouch. They hatch here and the male then takes care of them until they are ready to live independently. Members of this family feed on small invertebrates which are sucked into the tubular mouth.

1 COMMON SEAHORSE
Hippocampus kuda

This species is variable in colour and has small knobs on the corners of the bony plates. It grows to 30cm (12in), although appears shorter because the tail is coiled. *Ecology:* It occurs throughout the region and in the wider Indo-Pacific. It usually inhabits sheltered habitats, such as bays and estuaries, but may occasionally be found on outer reefs down to depths of 30m (100ft). Seagrasses or seaweed provide a favourite habitat.

2 RINGED PIPEFISH
Doryhampus dactyliophorus

This is one of several pipefish that has red and white bands on the body. It is most similar to the

Multi-banded Pipefish *D. multiannulatus,* but the latter species has a greater number of bands. The Ringed Pipefish grows to about 18cm (7in) long. *Ecology:* It occurs throughout the region and the wider Indo-Pacific, on reefs from shallow water to depths of about 60m (200ft). Like other pipefish, this species is shy and usually keeps close to the reef surface, often hiding in holes and crevices.

3 SCRIBBLED PIPEFISH
Corythoichthys intestinalis

The Scribbled Pipefish has intricate and variable dark marks on the body that are usually more distinct at the tail end. It reaches a length of about 16cm (6¼in). *Ecology:* It occurs throughout the region and also in the western Pacific, from shallow water to depths of about 20m (50ft), mainly on sandy and rubble areas.

FLATHEADS
Family Platycephalidae

Flatheads are closely related to scorpionfish, but have more elongated, flattened bodies with large, bizarrely ornamented heads. Sometimes all that is visible are the eyes and nostrils protruding from the sand. Even when lying out in the open, these fish are often difficult to spot because of their cryptic coloration. They are quite approachable and it may be possible to see the branched tassle-like 'eyelid' which helps to camouflage or shade the eye.

4 BEAUFORT'S CROCODILEFISH
Cymbacephalus beauforti

This species has a flattened head and body, and has tassles on the fins. It is mottled, usually a

greenish colour, for camouflage. It has a wide mouth and the eyes are positioned high on its head. It is a large species, growing to a length of about 50cm (1ft 8in). *Ecology:* It occurs throughout the region and also in the western Pacific, from shallow water to depths of about 30m (100ft).

1 Common Seahorse

2 Ringed Pipefish

3 Scribbled Pipefish

4 Beaufort's Crocodilefish – *(inset)* head detail

SCORPIONFISH, LIONFISH AND RELATIVES

Family Scorpaenidae

Most species in this family are well-built fish that are armed with venomous dorsal, anal and pelvic fin spines. They live on or close to the bottom and all are predators. Scorpionfish sit still and rely on excellent camouflage and quick reactions to snatch at fish and crustaceans, while lionfish often cruise above the reef surface and are more active in rounding up potential prey. This family is represented by about 30 species in the region.

1 RAGGY SCORPIONFISH
Scorpaenopsis venosa

This species gets its name from the skin flaps and tentacles on the head. The darkish mark on the soft dorsal fin, and the first three dorsal spines that step up evenly in length are usually diagnostic. Its maximum body length is about 18cm (7in). *Ecology:* It occurs throughout the region and the wider Indo-Pacific, on coastal reefs from shallow water to depths of about 25m (80ft).

2 LEAF SCORPIONFISH
Taenianotus triacanthus

This fish is easily distinguished by its compressed, leaf-like body and tall dorsal fin. It is usually a green or yellowish-brown colour, but occasionally red, white or black individuals are seen. The skin is covered with tiny papillae and the outer layer is shed periodically. Its maximum length is about 10cm (4in). *Ecology:* It is seen occasionally on reefs throughout the region and the wider Indo-Pacific, from shallow water to depths of over 100m (330ft). It usually rests on the bottom, swaying gently back and forth, then darting rapidly to catch small fish and crustaceans.

3 REEF STONEFISH
Synanceia verrucosa

The Reef Stonefish has a bulbous, warty body with a large pectoral fin. This grotesque-looking fish has spines with venom sacs at the base, and is renowned as probably the most venomous of all the world's fish. It is usually mottled greyish-brown in colour, but may have orange markings.

Ecology: It occurs throughout the region and the wider Indo-Pacific, usually in areas of shallow sand, weed and rubble, but to depths of 20m (50ft) or more. Stonefish are very well camouflaged and easily overlooked.

4 SPOTFIN LIONFISH
Pterois antennata

Lionfish are recognized by their large pectoral fins and long dorsal spines. Many are brightly coloured and have tentacles above the eyes. This species can be distinguished by the dark spots on the membrane between the pectoral rays. It grows to a length of about 20cm (8in). *Ecology:* It occurs throughout the region and the wider Indo-Pacific, from shallow water to depths of 50m (165ft) or more. It generally rests in caves and holes during the day and comes out to feed at dusk.

5 LIONFISH
Pterois volitans

This species has very prominent pectoral and dorsal fins patterned with dark red bands. The membranes between the pectoral rays are separate, giving them a feather-like appearance. It is one of the largest lionfish, growing to a length of over 35cm (14in). *Ecology:* It occurs throughout the region and western Pacific, from shallow water to depths of 50m (165ft) or more. It is replaced in the Indian Ocean and Red Sea by the very similar *P. miles*. Like other lionfish, *P. volitans* is fairly inactive during the day, but as the light dims it moves out into the open and begins hunting. These fish move slowly towards their prey with the pectoral fins spread wide, which helps herd the prey to a position where they can then be picked off easily.

1 Raggy Scorpionfish

2 Leaf Scorpionfish

3 Reef Stonefish

4 Spotfin Lionfish

5 Lionfish

ANTHIAS, GROUPERS AND SOAPFISH
Family Serranidae

Members of this diverse family range in size from a few centimetres to several metres in length. They have small scales and a single dorsal fin, often with a notch between the spiny and soft section. Serranids are carnivores, but prey varies from tiny planktonic crustaceans to big fish. The larger predators, such as groupers, are fairly large and heavily set. With their characteristically jutting lower jaw and large eyes these fish can look quite benign as they rest lazily on the bottom or drift gently close to recesses in the reef. But they are highly effective predators with a remarkable turn of speed when in hunting mode as they close in on their quarry, open their large mouths wide and suck the prey in. The social life of serranids involves a sex change. They are sequential hermaphrodites functioning first as females, then as males in later life.

1 SQUARESPOT ANTHIAS
Pseudanthias pleurotaenia

About 15 species of anthias occur in the region. All are small and colourful, with pointed tips to the tail lobes. The male Squarespot Anthias is easily recognized by the rectangular violet-magenta patch on the side of the body. Females are yellow with two parallel violet lines running from behind the eye to the tail base. The Squarespot Anthias grows to a length of about 20cm (8in). *Ecology:* It occurs throughout the region and also in the western Pacific. It is found on steep, outer slopes where it forms small aggregations, generally below 20m (50ft) depth. Like other anthias species, it feeds on plankton by day and moves into hiding places on the reef at night.

2 RED-CHEEKED ANTHIAS
Pseudanthias hutchii

Female Red-cheeked Anthias are greenish in colour with a yellow band on the cheek. Males are slightly larger and have a red stripe running from the eye on to the base of the pectoral fin, and a small red spot on the pectoral fin itself. They grow to a length of about 12cm (4¾in).

The Scalefin Anthias *P. squamipinnis* is similar, but rather varied in colour. Females are yellow-orange with a reddish stripe. Males usually have a purplish body, large red spot on the pectoral fin and an orange line running from the eye to the pectoral fin base. *Ecology:* The Red-cheeked Anthias occurs throughout the region and in the western Pacific and may be extremely numerous along the reef rim and upper slope of seaward reefs darting constantly back and forth as they feed on plankton. They live in 'harems' of one male and several subordinate females and juveniles.

3 PURPLE ANTHIAS
Pseudanthias tuka

This is one of several anthias to have a protruding upper lip. The male is bright purple with a yellowish lower jaw (males of *P. pascalus* are also purple, but they have a whitish, not yellow, chin). Female Purple Anthias are purple with a yellow strip along the top of the back, and yellow streaks on the tail (female *P. pascalus* have no yellow markings). *Ecology:* It occurs throughout the region and also in the western Pacific. It is found mainly on outer reefs where it forms small to large aggregations from shallow water to depths of over 30m (100ft).

1 Squarespot Anthias

2 Red-cheeked Anthias

3 Purple Anthias *(below)*

1 SLENDER GROUPER or WHITE-LINED ROCKCOD
Anyperodon leucogrammicus

The red spots, slender body and pointed head of this species make it unlikely to be confused with any of the other 60 or so species of rockcods and groupers that occur in the area. Juvenile Slender Groupers have white-and-yellow lines similar to certain non-fish-eating wrasses. It is thought that they mimic wrasse so that they can get close to unwary prey without frightening them off. Slender Groupers grow to a length of about 50cm (1ft 8in). *Ecology:* This is a fairly common fish on reefs throughout the region and the wider Indo-Pacific, from shallow water to depths of over 50m (165ft). It feeds mainly on other fish.

2 PEACOCK ROCKCOD
Cephalopholis argus

Cephalopholis species are medium-sized serranids with rounded tails. There are at least seven species in the area. The Peacock Rockcod can be recognized by the numerous dark-edged blue spots on the body and fins, and a white area in front of the pectoral fin. It grows to a length of about 40cm (16in). *Ecology:* It occurs on reefs throughout the region and the wider Indo-Pacific, from shallow water to depths of over 50m (165ft). It feeds mainly on fish.

3 CORAL COD
Cephalopholis miniata

Adult Coral Cod have evenly spaced, bright blue spots against a red background, but juveniles are less easily identified because they lack the spots. The Coral Cod grows to a length of about 40cm (16in). *Ecology:* It is a fairly common species on reefs throughout the region and the wider Indo-Pacific, from shallow water to depths of around 150m (500ft). It is often seen in the vicinity of caves on steep faces, and feeds mainly on fish.

4 HUMPBACK GROUPER or BARRAMUNDI COD
Cromileptes altivelis

The long, pointed head and concave profile above the eye make this species easily identifiable. The dark spots become smaller and more numerous with age. Its maximum length is about 70cm (2ft 4in). *Ecology:* It occurs on reefs throughout the region and the wider Indo-Pacific, but is generally uncommon. It is found both on coastal and seaward reefs, from shallow water to depths of at least 45m (150ft). It feeds on fish and crustaceans.

5 POTATO COD
Epinephelus tukula

Many species of *Epinephelus* occur in the region. All have 11 dorsal spines, but identification to species may not be easy. A few are easily recognized, but many have spots, blotches and bars that are not very distinctive between one species and another. The Potato Cod is identified by the small spots on the fins and the pale grey or whitish body with its large, black oval marks. It grows to a length of about 2m (6ft). *Ecology:* It occurs on reefs throughout the region and the wider Indo-Pacific, from shallow water to depths of over 150m (500ft). It is generally uncommon, but may be interested in divers. Feeding this species is potentially dangerous!

6 BLACKTIPPED ROCKCOD
Epinephelus fasciatus

The Blacktipped Rockcod is one of the smaller *Epinephelus* species, growing to a length of about 40cm (1ft 4in). Some specimens have a pale body with brown on the head, while others have reddish-brown bars, or may even be brownish-red overall without the bars. *Ecology:* It is fairly common throughout the region and the wider Indo-Pacific, especially on seaward reefs. It is found from shallow water to depths of at least 150m, (500ft) and feeds on crustaceans and fish.

1 Slender Grouper *(above left)*

2 Peacock Rockcod *(above)*

3 Coral Cod *(left)*

4 Humpback Grouper, juvenile

4 Humpback Grouper

5 Potato Cod

6 Blacktipped Rockcod

1 SPOTTED CORAL GROUPER
Plectropomus maculatus

At least five species of *Plectropomus* occur on reefs in the region. They are medium-sized groupers with only eight dorsal spines. The Spotted Coral Grouper has fewer, more widely spaced spots than other species, and those on the head are elongated. It reaches a length of about 70cm (2ft 4in). *Ecology:* It occurs on coastal reefs throughout the region and in the western Pacific.

2 SIX-LINED SOAPFISH
Grammistes sexlineatus

This is one of several soapfish in the area and is easily identified by its stripes. Like the others, it produces a bitter, poisonous mucus, which covers the skin and protects it from predators. It grows to about 30cm (12in) in length. *Ecology:* It occurs on reefs throughout the region, from shallow water to depths of over 150m (500ft). It hides in holes and crevices by day, emerging at night to hunt for crustaceans and fish.

LONGFINS AND PRETTYFINS
Family Plesiopidae

Members of this family are elongate fish with long pelvic fins. There are several species, but all are fairly small and easily overlooked due to their secretive habits.

3 COMET
Calloplesiops altivelis

The comet has an enlarged tail fin. If alarmed, it hides its head in a hole and changes the shape of its tail to resemble a moray eel's head to try to deter potential attackers. *Ecology:* It occurs on reefs throughout the region and the wider Indo-Pacific, from shallow water to depths of about 45m (150ft). It hides in holes and crevices by day, emerging at night to hunt for crustaceans and fish.

DOTTYBACKS
Family Pseudochromidae

All dottybacks are small, elongate, fish that hide amongst corals or in holes on the reef. Many are brightly coloured. When reproducing, females lay a ball of eggs on the reef surface which is guarded and moved if necessary by the male. About 20 species occur in the area.

4 PURPLE DOTTYBACK
Pseudochromis diadema

The purple back and yellow body of this species is distinctive. It grows to a length of about 6cm (2¼in). *Ecology:* It occurs on steep reef slopes, at depths below about 10m (33ft), where it hovers close to corals and rocks. It is restricted to the South-east Asian region.

5 ROYAL DOTTYBACK
Pseudochromis paccagnellae

This species is the same colour as the Purple Dottyback, but the purple is at the front end and the yellow is at the rear. It grows to a length of 7cm (2¾in). *Ecology:* It occurs on steep reef slopes throughout the region and also in the western Pacific, generally below about 10m (33ft) depth.

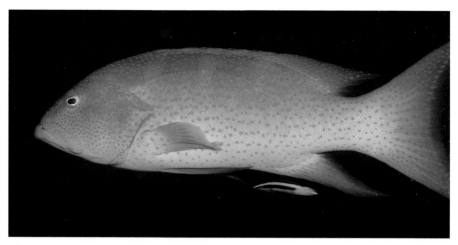

1 Spotted Coral Grouper

2 Six-lined Soapfish

3 Comet

4 Purple Dottyback

5 Royal Dottyback

HAWKFISH
Family Cirrhitidae

Hawkfish are small grouper-like fish with a continuous dorsal fin. Each of the ten dorsal fin spines has a cluster of tiny filaments at the tip. They have no air bladder and are poor swimmers, tending to sit still, resting on the stout lower portion of the pectoral fin as they lie in wait for small fish and crustaceans. Some species are serial hermaphrodites, with males having a territory and a harem of females. Around ten species occur in the region.

FRECKLED HAWKFISH
Paracirrhites forsteri

This species is recognized by its brown back, pale or yellowish belly and fins, and red spots on the head. The spots may be indistinct in juveniles, and the back redder. It grows to a length of about 20cm (8in). *Ecology:* It is fairly common on reefs throughout the region and also in the wider Indo-Pacific, from shallow water to depths of at least 35m (115ft). It perches on branching corals, but jumps off if divers get too close.

2 CORAL or DWARF HAWKFISH
Cirrhitichthys falco

There are several species of small hawkfish with reddish markings. This one can be distinguished by the reddish-brown, irregular saddles that taper towards its belly. It grows to a length of

about 7cm (2¾in). *Ecology:* It occurs on reefs throughout the region. It is found from shallow water to depths of at least 40m (130ft), usually perched near or on corals, where it lies in wait for shrimps and other small crustaceans.

3 LONGNOSE HAWKFISH
Oxycirrhitus typus

This species is easily recognized by its long nose. It grows to a length of about 13cm (5in). *Ecology:* It occurs on reefs throughout the region and the wider Indo-Pacific. It is always associated with large gorgonians and black corals occurring in steep, current-swept areas. Longnose Hawkfish may be seen at depths of about 10m (33ft), but generally they are in deeper water. They often live in monogamous pairs, with male and female in an exclusive mating arrangement. They feed on small bottom-dwelling or planktonic crustaceans.

CARDINALFISH
Family Apogonidae

Cardinalfish are small fish with prominent eyes, a large mouth and two dorsal fins. Most have one or more dark bands or dots near the base of the tail. An unusual feature of cardinalfish is that the male broods eggs in his mouth for about a week until they are ready to hatch into planktonic larvae. Possibly as many as 100 species occur in the area, but they are often hidden in caves during the day, emerging at night to feed on zooplankton.

4 RINGTAIL CARDINALFISH
Apogon aureus

Most *Apogon* species are striped, and it can be very difficult to distinguish one from another. This is one of the easier species to identify, due

to the dark ring around the base of the tail. It grows to a length of about 12cm (5in). *Ecology:* It occurs on sheltered reefs throughout the area and the wider Indo-Pacific, from shallow water to depths of about 50m (165ft). It remains close to shelter during the day, often around caves and in recesses in the reef.

1 Freckled Hawkfish

2 Coral Hawkfish *(below)*

3 Longnose Hawkfish

4 Ringtail Cardinalfish

1 BLACK-STRIPED CARDINALFISH
Apogon nigrofasciatus

The stripes on the body in this species are wider than in others, and do not converge onto the tail. Another feature is the absence of a black spot in the centre of the tail base. The Black-striped Cardinalfish grows to a length of about 10cm (4in). *Ecology:* It occurs on reefs throughout the region and the wider Indo-Pacific, from shallow water to depths of about 40m (130ft). It is usually fairly well hidden in shady recesses during the day.

2 PYJAMA or THREADFIN CARDINALFISH
Sphaeramia nematoptera

The deep body, tall fins and striking colour pattern of this species are unmistakable. It grows to a length of about 8cm (3in). *Ecology:* It occurs on sheltered reefs throughout the area and the wider Indo-Pacific, from shallow water to depths of about 30m (100ft). It is often seen in large aggregations amongst branching corals, such as *Acropora* and *Porites*.

BIGEYES
Family Priacanthidae

The body shape and habits of these fish are similar to soldierfish, but bigeyes are distinguished by the continuous dorsal fin, small scales, upturned mouth and even larger eyes. By day they rest in caves or close to coral. At night they move into open water to feed on large zooplankton. Bigeyes have a reflective tapetal layer in the eye, which almost doubles the amount of light detected. About six rather similar species occur in the region.

3 CRESCENT-TAIL BIGEYE
Priacanthus hamrur

As it name implies, this species has a distinctive, crescent-shaped tail. Its body colour can switch in an instant from deep red to silver or mottled silver, sometimes with dusky bars. It reaches a length of about 45cm (1ft 6in). *Ecology:* It occurs throughout the region and the wider Indo-Pacific, from shallow water to depths of over 70m (230ft), mainly on outer reefs.

SAND TILEFISH
Family Malacanthidae

These fish have an elongated body with a long, continuous dorsal fin and a long anal fin. They usually inhabit sandy or rubble areas on the deeper outer reef, where they construct burrows in which to hide, and also build large mounds as nests for the eggs. During the day they usually hover about 1m (3ft) above the burrow entrance. About eight species occur in the region.

4 BLUE TILEFISH
Hopiolatilus starcki

Juvenile Blue Tilefish are completely blue, but the rear part of the body becomes yellow as the fish grows and matures. It reaches a maximum length of approximately 15cm (6in). *Ecology:* It occurs throughout the region and western Pacific, on sand and rubble patches of steep reefs, from depths of about 30m (100ft) to at least 100m (330ft).

1 Black-striped Cardinalfish

2 Pyjama Cardinalfish

3 Crescent-tail Bigeye

4 Blue Tilefish

REMORAS
Family Echeneidae

Remoras are easily recognized by their highly modified spiny dorsal fin, which is formed into a long, ridged sucking disk. This is used for hitching rides on large fish, sea turtles, aquatic mammals and even divers, but they do no harm and can be easily dislodged.

1 SHARKSUCKER
Echeneis naucrates

This species is identified by the black longitudinal stripe and unique dorsal sucking disk. It reaches a length of about 1m (3ft). *Ecology:* It occurs in tropical and warm waters around the globe. The sharksucker feeds on scraps of food discarded by its host, and occasionally on external parasites.

JACKS AND TREVALLIES
Family Carangidae

Jacks are powerful swimmers that roam tropical and subtropical oceans, but they are regularly seen on reefs, particularly seaward ones with steep profiles. Dolphinfish, scad, pilotfish and pomfrets are included in this family. All have silvery, streamlined bodies, a narrow tail base and a forked tail. Most have bony plates (scutes) along the midline of the tail stem and some have a single small finlet dorsally and ventrally (but not a long series of finlets as in the tunas). Most jacks are fish hunters, often patrolling the reef edge in schools. They have a wide range and several are found throughout the tropics. Probably over 50 species occur in the region.

2 BIGEYE TREVALLY
Caranx sexfasciatus

Adults are silvery, but juveniles may have five or six dusky bars. The eyes are larger than in most other species. Other identifying features are the white tip to the dorsal fin lobe, and the black spot on the upper edge of the gill cover. The Bigeye grows to a length of 85cm (2ft 9in). *Ecology:* It occurs throughout the region and the wider Indo-Pacific. Juveniles tend to be found in shallower, inshore areas but adults move to deeper reefs, especially drop-offs, and are found to depths of at least 100m (330ft). It is one of the commonest trevallies in the area, often forming huge schools.

3 GOLDBODY TREVALLY
Carangoides bajad

Several trevallies are spotted with yellow, but this one is recognized by the haphazard arrangement of the spots and the golden or dusky yellow body colour. It reaches a maximum length of 45cm (1ft 6in) *Ecology:* Juveniles tend to be solitary, and are found on coastal reefs, but adults move to steep seaward reefs where they usually gather in small groups from shallow water to depths of about 50m (165ft). They occur throughout the region and also the Indian Ocean. Similarly coloured Yellow Goatfish sometimes mingle with this species.

4 RAINBOW RUNNER
Elegatis bipinnulata

The Rainbow Runner is easily recognized by its elongate, streamlined body with yellow-and-blue stripes. Another feature is the presence of small, separate finlets on the tail base. It grows to a length of about 125cm (4ft). *Ecology:* It occurs throughout the region and in all tropical seas from the surface to depths of over 150m (500ft). It usually roams in large schools, feeding on pelagic crustaceans and small fish.

1 Sharksucker *(top)*; on shark *(above)*

3 Goldbody Trevally

2 Bigeye Trevally

4 Rainbow Runners

SNAPPERS
Family Lutjanidae

Snappers are perch-like fish with a continuous dorsal fin, a strongly or slightly forked tail, and a large mouth with well-developed canine teeth in both jaws. Snappers tend to aggregate around reefs during the day, drifting gently as they rest in shady places. They then disperse at night to feed on invertebrates, such as crustaceans, gastropods, sea urchins, octopus and small fish. Probably around 50 species occur in the area. They are popular food fish.

1 BLUE-STRIPED SNAPPER
Lutjanus kasmira

Several species of yellow-and-blue-striped snappers occur in the region. This species has only four stripes and differs from *L. bengalensis* (also with four stripes) by the presence of yellow on the belly under the lower stripe. The Bluestriped Snapper reaches a length of about 21cm (8¼in). *Ecology:* It occurs throughout the region and the wider Indo-Pacific, from shallow water to depths of over 250m (820ft). These fish often gather in large aggregations during the day, close to prominent reef features, or around wrecks.

2 TWO-SPOT SNAPPER
Lutjanus biguttatus

This small snapper is easily recognized by its distinctive colour pattern. It reaches a length of about 20cm (8in). *Ecology:* It occurs on reefs throughout the region and also in the eastern Indian Ocean and western Pacific, from shallow water to depths of about 35m.

3 CHEQUERED SNAPPER
Lutjanus decussatus

This species is easily recognized by the pattern of longitudinal and vertical stripes, and the black blotch on the tail base. It grows to a length of about 30cm (12in). *Ecology:* It occurs mainly in the South-east Asian region, but also in the eastern Indian Ocean and western Pacific, from shallow water to depths of about 30m (100ft). Juveniles are found mainly on the shallow reef flat.

4 MIDNIGHT SNAPPER
Macolor macularis

The Midnight Snapper is sometimes confused with the Black Snapper, because both species have a dark body colour and deep profile. The Midnight Snapper is distinguished by its yellow eye and the yellowish head patterned with thin blue lines. Juveniles in both species are black and white, but the Midnight Snapper has higher fins and a clear (not black) pectoral fin. It grows to a length of about 55cm (1ft 10in). *Ecology:* It occurs throughout the region and the wider Indo-Pacific, from shallow water to depths of at least 50m (165ft).

5 BLACK SNAPPER
Macolor niger

The black pectoral fin and broad white bar behind the eye are good identification features for the juvenile of this species. The adult is dark overall, without the yellow eye and markings on the head described for the Midnight Snapper. It grows to a length of about 60cm (2ft). *Ecology:* It occurs throughout the region and the wider Indo-Pacific, from shallow water to depths of at least 50m (165ft). Juveniles are usually solitary, but adults tend to form small groups on steep outer reefs. They feed on large zooplankton, mainly at night.

Snappers

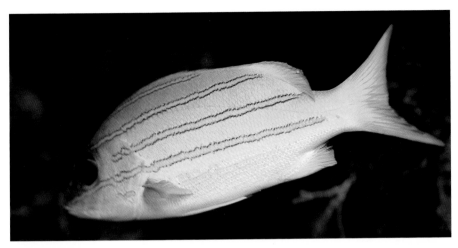

1 Blue-striped Snapper

2 Two-spot Snapper

3 Chequered Snapper

4 Midnight Snapper, adult *(left)*

5 Black Snapper, juvenile *(above)*

FUSILIERS
Family Caesionidae

Fusiliers are related to snappers, but are more elongate and have smaller mouths. They are fast swimmers and are constantly on the move as they search for plankton. About 16 species occur in the region, and some of them form mixed schools.

YELLOWBACK FUSILIER
Caesio teres

Several similar fusiliers occur in the area. Juvenile Yellowbacks have more yellow than the adult, but it does not extend above the eye as it does in *Pterocaesio xanthonota*. Adult Yellowbacks are similar to *C. cuning*, but the latter has a deeper profile and distinct blue marks on the face. The Yellowback Fusilier reaches a length of about 30cm (12in). *Ecology:* It occurs around reefs throughout the region and the wider Indo-Pacific, from shallow water to depths of about 40m (130ft). Juveniles usually occur singly or in small groups, but adults form large schools.

MARR'S FUSILIER
Pterocaesio marri

Marr's Fusilier is one of several species that have black tips to the tail-fin lobes. Yellow stripes are also present in a number of species. *P. marri* has two yellow lines, both of which end close to the edge of the gill cover. In *P. diagramma* the lower yellow stripe extends through the eye. Marr's Fusilier reaches a length of about 32cm (12½in). *Ecology:* It occurs around reefs throughout the region and the wider Indo-Pacific, from shallow water to depths of about 25m (80ft).

NEON FUSILIER
Pterocaesio tile

The bright colours of this species make it one of the more easily identified fusiliers, although the brightness of the iridescent blue band along each side of the fish can vary. The extent and intensity of the red on the belly also changes, becoming particularly bright at night. A dark streak is always present along the edge of each tail fin. It grows to a maximum length of about 25cm (10in). *Ecology:* It occurs around reefs throughout the region and wider Indo-Pacific, from shallow water to depths of about 25m (80ft). It sometimes forms large aggregations on outer reef slopes.

SWEETLIPS
Family Haemulidae

Sweetlips are medium- to large-sized fish, quite similar to snappers, but they can be distinguished by the thickened lips, deep body and high (convex) head profile. Most undergo a dramatic change in colour pattern from juvenile to adult. Their food also switches from zooplankton to bottom-dwelling invertebrates. There are about 16 species in the region.

HARLEQUIN SWEETLIPS
Plectorhinchus chaetodontoides

Several sweetlips have spots, but those of this species are bigger than in other species and extend further down the fish's side. Juveniles are brown with white blotches and the intermediate stage is white with large black spots. The Harlequin reaches a length of over 60cm (2ft). *Ecology:* It occurs on reefs throughout the region and in the wider Indo-Pacific, from shallow water to depths of about 50m (165ft). Juveniles usually hide amongst corals on coastal or lagoonal reefs, while adults are found on seaward reefs.

1 Yellowback Fusilier

2 Marr's Fusilier

3 Neon Fusilier

4 Harlequin Sweetlips

RIBBON SWEETLIPS
Plectorhinchus polytaenia

The closely set, black-edged, yellow-and-white lines make this species easily identifiable. The juve-nile is similar to the adult but has fewer lines. It reaches a length of over 45cm (1ft 6in). *Ecology:* It occurs on reefs throughout the region and as far south as north-west Australia, from depths of about 5–40m (15–130ft), on both coastal and seaward reefs.

SPINECHEEKS
Family Nemipteridae

These small to medium-sized fish are elongate, with a single dorsal fin, large scales and a small mouth. Most are white or pale with brownish or yellow markings. The family includes monocle bream and spinecheeks, whiptails and threadfin breams (*Nemipterus* spp.). Many live in deep water, but about 25 species occur on reefs in the region.

TWO-LINE SPINECHEEK
Scolopsis bilineatus

This species has a distinctive black-edged line running from beneath the eye to the middle of the back. There are also two shorter white lines. In juveniles, the lines extend all the way to the back of the rear dorsal fin. It grows to a length of about 23cm (9in). *Ecology:* One of the commonest species in the region, also occurring in the Indian Ocean and western Pacific. It is found from shallow water to depths of about 25m (80ft).

THREE-STRIPED WHIPTAIL
Pentapodus trivittatus

The vertical and horizontal markings show up most distinctly in the juvenile, becoming paler in the adult. This species has a slim body and reaches a length of about 25cm (10in). *Ecology:* It occurs throughout the region and also in the western Pacific. Juveniles are usually found in groups in very shallow coastal habitats, while the adults occur singly on reefs to depths of about 15m (50ft). They feed on zooplankton.

EMPERORS
Family Lethrinidae

Emperors occur only in the Indo-Pacific and are medium-sized fish similar in appearance to snappers, but with slightly thickened lips and a more pointed mouth. Juveniles are usually quite different in appearance to the adults, and many adults can change colour rapidly, so making identification difficult. Over 25 species occur around reefs in the area.

BIGEYE EMPEROR
Monotaxis grandoculis

The large eye is very distinctive. Adults are pale or silvery, sometimes with wide dusky bars showing; juveniles have much more distinct markings. It grows to a length of about 60cm (2ft). *Ecology:* It occurs on reefs throughout the region and the wider Indo-Pacific, from shallow water to depths of around 100m (330ft). Juveniles are solitary, but adults often hover in small groups during the day. At night they move away to sandy areas to feed on molluscs and other hard-shelled invertebrates.

1 Ribbon Sweetlips

2 Two-line Spinecheek

3 Three-striped Whiptail

4 Bigeye Emperor

1 YELLOWSPOT or GOLD-LINED EMPEROR
Gnathodentex aurolineatus

This species is readily identified by the large yellow spot on the tail base, but the rest of the body varies to match the background, being pale in sandy habitats and darker on the reef slope. It grows to a length of about 30cm (12in). *Ecology:* It occurs on reefs throughout the region and the wider Indo-Pacific, from shallow water to depths of around 30m (100ft). They usually gather in aggregations during the day, drifting just above the coral, then move away to sandy areas at night to feed on reef invertebrates.

2 ORANGEFIN EMPEROR
Lethrinus erythracanthus

The dark body and orange or yellow fin distinguish this species. It is one of the larger emperors, growing to a length of about 70cm (2ft 4in). *Ecology:* It occurs on reefs throughout the region and the wider Indo-Pacific, from depths of around 15–120m (50–400ft). It is a solitary fish by habit, remaining close to the reef slope during the day. Like other emperors, it feeds on bottom-dwelling invertebrates, such as worms, molluscs, crabs and shrimps, and occasionally on small fish, doing most of its hunting at night.

GOATFISH
Family Mullidae

Goatfish have an elongate body, two dorsal fins, and two prominent barbels under the chin. The latter are not always visible because they can be tucked away between the lower parts of the gill cover when not in use. Although goatfish are sometimes seen around reefs, most are associated with sandy habitats, where they use the barbels to hunt out small buried organisms. The barbels, which are also used by males to attract females, move independently and bear numerous sense organs. Once prey, such as crustaceans and molluscs, have been located they are either 'excavated' or blown out of the sand, so that they can be captured. Other fish, especially wrasse, often hang around goatfish as they feed, in the hope of a free meal. Some goatfish feed mainly at night, and nocturnal coloration is usually confusingly different from during the day. Over 17 species of goatfish occur in the area.

3 DASH-DOT GOATFISH
Parupeneus barberinus

Several goatfish have a dark spot on the tail and a dark line along the side of the body, but this species is the only one where the line extends right through the eye to the mouth. It is one of the largest goatfish, growing to a length of about 50cm (1ft 8in). *Ecology:* It is common throughout the region and the wider Indo-Pacific, on sandy patches from shallow water to depths of around 100m (330ft).

4 YELLOWFIN GOATFISH
Mulloidichthys vanicolensis

This species is distinguished from the similar-looking *M. flavolineatus* by its short snout and the absence of a black spot below the first dorsal fin. It reaches a length of about 38cm (1ft 3in). *Ecology:* It occurs throughout the region and the wider Indo-Pacific, on sandy patches from shallow water to depths of around 120m (400ft). It is fairly inactive during the day, swimming slowly in large aggregations above the bottom and then dispersing at night to feed.

1 Yellowspot Emperor

2 Orangefin Emperor

3 Dash-dot Goatfish

4 Yellowfin Goatfish

BATFISH
Family Ephippidae

Batfish have a deep, rounded, laterally compressed body. The dorsal and anal fin of juveniles is extraordinarily long, but becomes proportionally smaller as the fish grows. Three species of about the same size occur in the region. They are greyish with darker markings.

PINNATE BATFISH
Platax pinnatus

The Pinnate Batfish is distinguished by the concave profile of its snout, which in other species is rounded or convex. It grows to a length of about 50cm (1ft 8in). The juvenile is easily recognized by the bright red margin to its fins and body. When very small it swims on its side with an undulating motion that is thought to protect it, because it mimics a toxic flatworm and so is avoided by predators. *Ecology:* It occurs throughout the region and in the western Pacific. Juveniles are found in sheltered habitats, such as mangroves and inner reefs, while adults live on the reef to depths of at least 20m (50ft), generally in steep areas with overhangs that provide shelter. They are omnivores, picking at algae and small invertebrates on the reef surface.

SWEEPERS
Family Pempheridae

Sweepers are small fish with deep, compressed bodies, a long anal fin and short, high dorsal fin. The large eyes give them the alternative name of 'bulls-eyes'. They rest by day in caverns on the reef slope, sometimes in huge numbers. At night they disperse to feed on plankton, either individually or in loose aggregations. Some sweepers have bioluminescent organs associated with the gut.

GOLDEN or PYGMY SWEEPER
Parapriacanthus ransonneti

The Golden Sweeper is less deep-bodied than other species, and is also smaller, with a maximum length of about 10cm (4in). *Ecology:* It occurs throughout the region and the wider Indo-Pacific, mainly on steep reefs from depths of about 10–50m (30–165ft). During the day, it often gathers in large schools that drift back and forth in caves and other shady places, reacting in unison to the presence of divers. It emerges at night to feed on zooplankton.

CHUB
Family Kyphosidae

    Chub (sometimes called rudderfish) have a relatively deep body with a continuous dorsal fin. The head is pointed and the mouth relatively small. Several similar species of *Kyphosus* occur in the region, and they are not easy to tell apart on visual observation alone. Rudderfish are particularly common on surf-swept reef flats, where they feed on a wide variety of algae, including large plants such as *Turbinaria* and *Sargassum*. They move to these feeding grounds with the rising tide, and at other times are seen on the seaward reef front.

1 Pinnate Batfish, juvenile

1 Pinnate Batfish, intermediate phase

2 Golden Sweeper

3 Chub

BUTTERFLYFISH
Family Chaetodontidae

Butterflyfish have a deep and extremely compressed body, and a small terminal mouth with fine brush-like teeth. They have perfected the art of masking the eyes with a dark stripe to confuse potential predators. These so-called 'eyebars' conceal the location of the real eyes, which are thought to be used as 'targets' by predatory fish. Butterflyfish move around the reef during the day, either singly or in pairs. They feed on a range of small food items, including coral polyps, the tube feet of sea urchins, small crabs and filamentous algae.

Most have a territory or home range that they defend. Studies on the behaviour of some coral-feeding species show that they often follow specific paths when foraging over the reef, moving from one food patch to another in a set routine. If a coral that they use as a landmark is removed, they look for it, then move on, picking up their route at the first opportunity.

Butterflyfish often occur in male-female pairs, and the pairs may remain together for several years, sometimes for life. At night they retreat to safe places amongst rocks and coral and many adopt a different colour pattern. Over 55 species of butterflyfish occur in the region.

1 BLACK-BACKED BUTTERFLYFISH
Chaetodon melannotus

The presence of a black area beneath the dorsal fin distinguishes this species from *C. ocellicaudus,* which has diagonal black lines and a black spot on the tail base, but no dark shading. The Black-backed Butterflyfish grows to a length of about 15cm (6in). *Ecology:* It occurs on reefs throughout the region and the wider Indo-Pacific, from shallow water to depths of about 30m (100ft), usually in pairs but sometimes in groups. This species feeds on hard and soft coral polyps.

2 BENNETT'S BUTTERFLYFISH
Chaetodon bennetti

There are several other species of butterflyfish that have a large black spot on the back, but the two curved blue lines in this species are distinctive. It grows to a length of about 18cm (7in). *Ecology:* It is an uncommon inhabitant of reefs throughout the region and the wider Indo-Pacific, seen singly or in pairs. The juvenile is generally found amongst branching corals in shallow water, while the adult occurs to a depth of about 30m (100ft). It feeds primarily on coral polyps.

3 PANDA BUTTERFLYFISH
Chaetodon adiergastos

Several species have a panda-like black mark through the eye, but this one is easily recognized by its yellow fins and the whitish body with grey diagonal lines. It grows to a length of about 18cm (7in). *Ecology:* It occurs on reefs in Indonesia and the eastern and northern parts of the region, from shallow water to depths of about 25m (80ft). It feeds on a mixture of coral polyps and small invertebrates.

4 TRIANGULAR BUTTERFLYFISH
Chaetodon baronessa

The deep body and close-set lines on the body are distinctive, but this species may be confused with *C. triangulum,* which is identical except for a broad dark patch on the tail – rather than the thin line in the Triangular Butterflyfish. Both species reach a maximum length of about 15cm (6in). *Ecology:* This species occurs in the east of the region, and in the western Pacific, while *C. triangulum* is found in the far west (Java) and in the Indian Ocean. Both species live on shallow reefs with high coral cover. They feed exclusively on coral polyps, primarily table *Acropora*.

Butterflyfish

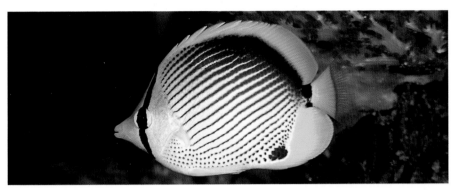

1 Black-backed Butterflyfish

2 Bennett's Butterflyfish *(below)*

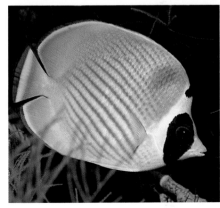

3 Panda Butterflyfish

4 Triangular Butterflyfish

1 ORNATE BUTTERFLYFISH
Chaetodon ornatissimus

The broad yellow stripes on the body make this species easily identifiable, and distinguish it from *C. meyeri* which has black stripes. It grows to a length of about 20cm (8in). *Ecology:* It occurs on reefs throughout the region and also in the central Indian Ocean and much of the Pacific. The juvenile is solitary and is generally found amongst branching corals in shallow water, while the adults occur in pairs at depths down to at least 35m (115ft). They feed primarily on coral polyps within a well-defined 'home range'.

2 ORANGE-BANDED CORALFISH
Coradion chrysozonus

Coradion species have relatively high bodies, with several bands in addition to the one through the eye. The Orange-banded Coralfish is distinguished from the other two species that occur in the region by the presence of a single black eyespot on the soft dorsal fin. It reaches a maximum length of about 15cm (6in). *Ecology:* It occurs on reefs throughout the region and also in the western Pacific, from depths of about 3–60m (10–200ft). It feeds mainly on small invertebrates living amongst sponges, and is often seen in areas where coral growth is not particularly prolific.

3 BEAKED CORALFISH
Chelmon rostratus

This is an easily identified species – no others in the region have the long nose and four golden-yellow bars. It is one of the more inquisitive butterflyfish, and may come quite close to divers. It reaches a length of about 20cm (8in). *Ecology:* It occurs on reefs throughout the region and also in the Andaman Sea and southwards to Australia. It is generally seen on sheltered inner reefs, from shallow water to depths of about 25m (80ft), where it feeds on coral polyps and small invertebrates.

4 BIG LONG-NOSED BUTTERFLYFISH
Forcipiger longirostris

This species, as its name implies, is better endowed than the 'ordinary' long-nosed butterflyfish, *F. flavissimus*. When both species are seen together the difference is obvious. The Big Long-nosed also has rows of very small black dots on the white portion in front of the pectoral fin. It reaches a length of about 22cm (8½in). *Ecology:* Long-nosed butterflyfish occur throughout the region and the wider Indo-Pacific, from shallow water to depths of over 60m (200ft). They are often seen in steep areas, near caves, and their diet consists mainly of small crustaceans, which they extract from crevices in the reef and between coral branches, using the long snout as a probe.

5 PYRAMID BUTTERFLYFISH
Hemitaurichthys polylepis

The unusual colour and habits of this species make it easily identified. It grows to a length of about 18cm (7in). *Ecology:* It occurs on outer, current-swept reefs throughout the region and western Pacific, usually in large aggregations above the reef where it feeds on zooplankton.

6 LONGFIN BANNERFISH
Heniochus acuminatus

Bannerfish get their name from the elongate extensions to the first few spines of the dorsal fin. To complicate matters, several species lack this 'banner', even though they have the characteristic bannerfish body shape. The Longfin Bannerfish has the longest banner of all species in the area, and two broad bars with a small black mark above the eye. It reaches a length of about 20cm (8in). *Ecology:* It occurs on reefs throughout the region and the wider Indo-Pacific, from shallow water to depths of about 75m (245ft). It looks very similar to the Schooling Bannerfish, *H. diphreutes*, but can usually be distinguished by the fact that it occurs singly or in pairs, rather than in aggregations. It feeds on zooplankton.

1 Ornate Butterflyfish

2 Orange-banded Coralfish

3 Beaked Coralfish

4 Big Long-nosed Butterflyfish

5 Pyramid Butterflyfish

6 Longfin Bannerfish

ANGELFISH
Family Pomacanthidae

Angelfish are superficially similar to butterflyfish, but can readily be distinguished by the prominent spine on the edge of the gill cover. They are important browsers on attached life, especially sponges, and some juveniles may act as cleaners. Angelfish are hermaphrodites. Most are territorial and live in 'harems' of a single male with several females. Adult angelfish are easily identified by colour, but juveniles can sometimes be confused with each other or other families altogether. About 27 species occur in the region.

1 THREE-SPOT ANGELFISH
Apolemichthys trimaculatus

The juvenile is yellow with a series of narrow reddish bars but no blue nose. The yellow body and blue nose of the adult make it instantly recognizable. It grows to a length of about 25cm (10in). *Ecology:* It occurs on reefs throughout the region, Indian Ocean and western Pacific, generally below a depth of about 20m (65ft). It feeds mainly on sponges and tunicates.

2 VERMICULATED ANGELFISH
Chaetodontoplus mesoleucus

The size, body shape and presence of a dark bar through the eye means that this angelfish is sometimes mistaken for a butterflyfish. It grows to a length of 18cm (7in). *Ecology:* It occurs on reefs throughout the region, mainly on protected continental shelf sites, from shallow water to depths of about 20m (50ft). It feeds on algae and attached animals, including sponges and tunicates, usually moving around singly or in small groups.

3 SIX-BANDED ANGELFISH
Pomacanthus sextriatus

The juvenile has white lines on a dark bluish-black background, and closely resembles the juvenile of several other species. It begins to change into the adult coloration at a length of about 8–15cm (3–6in). Its maximum size is about 45cm (1ft 6in). *Ecology:* It occurs in a wide range of habitats on reefs throughout the region and in the western Pacific. Adults are often in pairs and occur at depths of about 3–50m (10–165ft), but juveniles are mainly in shallow water and usually single.

4 MAJESTIC ANGELFISH
Pomacanthus navarchus

The juvenile has narrow vertical pale blue lines separated by dark blue bands. The tail is clear. It begins to change into the adult colours at 3–8cm (1–3in), and the adult grows to a length of 28cm (11in). *Ecology:* It occurs in the east of the region, from Indonesia through to the western Pacific. The juvenile is usually in shallow, sheltered habitats, but the adult is found on a range of reef types from shallow water to depths of about 40m (130ft). It feeds mainly on sponges and tunicates.

5 REGAL ANGELFISH
Pygoplites diacanthus

The juvenile is similar to the adult except for a large eyespot on the soft dorsal fin. The adult is one of the most brightly coloured and distinctive angelfish. It grows to a length of about 25cm (10in). *Ecology:* It occurs on reefs throughout the region and the wider Indo-Pacific, from shallow water to depths of about 50m (165ft), often in the vicinity of steep faces. It feeds on sponges and tunicates.

6 LAMARCK'S ANGELFISH
Genicanthus lamarck

Several *Genicanthus* species occur in the area. They have elongate bodies and tails with long filaments, and lack the vivid colours of other angelfish. Lamarck's is easily recognized by the four black lines on the body, black pelvic fins and black dorsal fin. It grows to a length of 23cm (9in). *Ecology:* It occurs throughout the region and the wider Indo-Pacific. It forms aggregations above steep outer reefs, where it feeds on zooplankton.

Angelfish

1 Three-spot Angelfish

2 Vermiculated Angelfish

3 Six-banded Angelfish

4 Majestic Angelfish

5 Regal Angelfish

6 Lamarck's Angelfish *(right)*

DAMSELFISH AND ANEMONEFISH
Family Pomacentridae

Pomacentrids are small fish with oval to elongated bodies and a small terminal mouth.

ANEMONEFISH

Anemonefish (clownfish) spend their entire set-tled life in association with giant anemones and are found only in the Indo-Pacific. Twenty-eight species are known; 13 occur in South-east Asia. The fish benefit by having a safe home where they can feed and nest without being attacked. The anemone stings intruders, yet the clownfish can 'bathe' freely in the tentacles without being stung because of their protective mucous covering. Not only is the layer thicker than usual, but its chemical make-up prevents the anemone's stinging cells from being acti-vated. Anemonefish live in pairs or groups and have a social life that involves sex change and female dominance. The female is the largest, and she controls the sexual development of others. The next biggest functions as a male, but has undeveloped ovaries and immediately changes sex should the dominant female dis-appear. At the same time, the dominant juve-nile develops into a male. This means that a breeding pair is virtually always present and that egg laying can go on uninterrupted. A nest may be visible at the base of the anemone. This is guarded for about a week before the eggs hatch. The larvae spend about a week floating in the plankton, and then seek out a suitable host by smell, rather than by sight.

1 FALSE CLOWN ANEMONEFISH
Amphiprion ocellaris

This is the most brightly coloured anemonefish in the area, with its orange body and three white bars. The Clown Anemonefish *A. percula* is very similar but has a wider black edge to the fins. They both grow to a length of about 11cm (4¼in). *Ecology:* The False Clown occurs on reefs throughout the region to Indonesia and north Australia, and also in the eastern Indian Ocean. The Clown Anemonefish is found in Papua New Guinea, Queensland and the western Pacific. These anemonefish occur with several species of

anemone, and both occur from shallow water to depths of about 15m (50ft).

2 PINK ANEMONEFISH

This species is pinkish orange in colour with a sin-gle white line along the top of the head and body, and a narrow vertical bar through the eye. Its max-imum length is about 10cm (4in). *A. sandaraci-nos* is similar but lacks the vertical bar. *Ecology:* restricted to the South-east Asian region. It occurs with four species of giant anemone, on reefs and sandy patches to depths of about 30m (100ft).

3 TOMATO ANEMONEFISH
Amphiprion frenatus

There are two species of anemonefish in the region that have a single white bar and a dark body. The Tomato Anemonefish has orange anal and pelvic fins, but these are black in the other species, the Dusky Anemonefish *A. melanopus*. The Tomato Anemonefish grows to a length of about 14cm (5½in). *Ecology:* It occurs through-out the region and in the extreme western Pacif-ic, mainly on sheltered, shallow inshore reefs. It is found almost exclusively with the anemone *Entacmaea quadricolor.*

4 SPINE-CHEEK ANEMONEFISH
Premnas biaculeatus

Young fish are bright red with three narrow white bars. The larger female fish are darker and the bars are often indistinct, but can 'flash' white if the fish is agitated. Its maximum length is about 16cm (6¼in). Unlike *Amphiprion* species, *Prem-nas* species have a distinct spine on the gill cover. *Ecology:* It is found in the South-east Asian region and down to northern Queensland. It associates only with *Entacmaea quadricolor,* which occurs on reefs to depths of about 15m (50ft).

1 False Clown Anemonefish

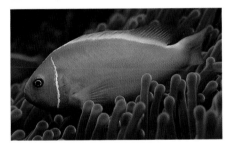

2 Pink Anemonefish

3 Tomato Anemonefish

4 Spine-cheek Anemonefish

DAMSELFISH

There are about 335 species of damselfish worldwide, of which at least 150 occur in Southeast Asia. They are found in a wide range of habitats and will be seen on every dive. Some form aggregations in mid-water where they feed on plankton. Others are omnivores or herbivores and stay close to the bottom. These species are often territorial and some are so aggressive that they will readily take on intruding divers.

It is not uncommon to see damselfish spawning. Once a nest has been prepared, the male becomes very excitable, jumping and circling to attract a female. Courting damselfish make chirping sounds, which vary between species. After the female has deposited her eggs the male fertilizes them and then cares for them until they hatch. The larvae float in the plankton for about a week before settling on the reef.

1 SCISSORTAIL SERGEANT
Abudefduf sexfasciatus

This species is distinguished from the other four sergeant major species found in the area by the black edges to the tail-fin lobes. The Indo-Pacific Sergeant also has five bars, but lacks these tail markings. The Scissortail Sergeant reaches a length of about 22cm (8½in). *Ecology:* It is common throughout the region, and also occurs in the wider Indo-Pacific. Adults form aggregations above coral and rocky reefs, to depths of about 15m (50ft). They feed on plankton but also browse on benthic algae and small invertebrates.

2 INDO-PACIFIC SERGEANT
Abudefduf vaigensis

This species has five bars, a pale tail and yellowish back. It grows to a length of about 22cm (8½in). *Ecology:* It is common throughout the region, and also occurs in the wider Indo-Pacific. Adults form aggregations above coral and rocky reefs, to depths of about 12m (40ft). They feed on plankton but also browse on benthic algae and small invertebrates.

3 STAGHORN DAMSEL
Amblyglyphidodon curacao

There are a number of *Amblyglyphidodon* species in the area, all of which have relatively deep bodies. The Staghorn Damsel is recognized by the greenish-yellow body colour and the broad alternating bars, which are not black as in the sergeant majors. It reaches a length of about 13cm (5in). *Ecology:* It is found throughout the region and the wider Indo-Pacific, and is often quite common. Adults generally gather in aggregations above coral and rocky reefs, where they feed on plankton.

4 GOLDEN DAMSEL
Amblyglyphidodon aureus

This species is yellow overall with a black eye. It grows to a length of about 14cm (5½in). *Ecology:* It occurs on reefs throughout the region, and also in the eastern Indian Ocean and western Pacific. It is generally seen on steep seaward reefs and passages, at about 10–50m (33–165ft) depth, but sometimes shallower. Juveniles often seek shelter, while adults venture further from the reef face in search of plankton. They generally form loose groups of several individuals.

5 DARKFIN CHROMIS
Chromis atripes

Like other *Chromis* species, this one has an oval body and a forked tail. There are a number of similar species, but the Darkfin Chromis can usually be identified by the dark margins to the soft dorsal and anal fins. It grows to a length of about 7cm (2¾in). *Ecology:* It occurs throughout the region and also in the western Pacific, from shallow water to depths of about 40m (130ft), especially on seaward reefs. It feeds on plankton and generally moves around alone, just off the reef face.

2 Indo-Pacific Sergeant

1 Scissortail Sergeant

3 Staghorn Damsel

4 Golden Damsel

5 Darkfin Chromis

1 TERNATE CHROMIS
Chromis ternatensis

This is one of several *Chromis* that have dark margins to the tail-fin lobes. It grows to about 10cm (4in). *Ecology:* It is found on reefs throughout the region and the wider Indo-Pacific, from shallow water to depths of about 35m (115ft). Individuals gather in small groups and are often associated with *Acropora* and other branching corals.

2 BLUE DEVIL
Chrysiptera cyanea

Pomacentrid species belonging to the genus *Chrysiptera* have a fairly narrow body, and many are coloured blue or yellow. The Blue Devil is bright blue with an orange tail in the male. It grows to a length of about 8cm (3in). *Ecology:* This species is found on reefs throughout the region and in the western Pacific, from shallow water to depths of about 8m (26ft), usually in groups. It feeds mainly on plankton but also picks at algae and invertebrates on the reef surface.

3 THREESPOT DASCYLLUS
Dascyllus trimaculatus

The white spots are prominent in juveniles but gradually fade as the fish grows. Like other *Dascyllus* it is deep bodied and has a high forehead. It grows to a length of about 14cm (5½in). *Ecology:* It occurs on reefs throughout the region and the wider Indo-Pacific, from shallow water to depths of about 55m (180ft). Juveniles often associate with branching corals or giant anemones, while older fish gather in groups around prominent features, such as coral mounds. They feed mainly on zooplankton.

4 WHITE DAMSEL
Dischistodus perspicillatus

Like others in the genus *Dischistodus,* the White Damsel is fairly drab in colour, being whitish overall, with several dark spots on the top of the back and head. It grows to a length of about 20cm (8in). *Ecology:* It is found throughout the region and in the eastern Indian Ocean and western Pacific, occurring in shallow, sheltered habitats to depths of about 10m (33ft). It feeds on algae and tends 'gardens' in rocky or rubble areas, defending its territory from other herbivores.

5 BEHN'S DAMSEL
Neoglyphidodon nigroris

The juveniles are very distinctive and colourful in this species, but the adult is mainly brown. It grows to a length of about 13cm (5in). *Ecology:* It occurs on reefs throughout the region and in the eastern Indian Ocean and western Pacific, from shallow water to depths of about 20m (65ft). It is usually solitary and has a mixed diet of algae, plankton and small crustaceans.

6 PRINCESS DAMSEL
Pomacentrus vaiuli

This species reaches a length of about 9cm (3½in), and is is one of many *Pomacentrus* that occur in the area. It is bluish-brown overall, but the intensity of the colour varies considerably. A large white-edged, dark blue spot is present at the rear of the dorsal fin. *Ecology:* It is found on reefs throughout the region and in the western Pacific, from shallow water to depths of about 40m (130ft). It is usually seen alone, close to the reef surface, where it browses on algae and small invertebrates.

1 Ternate Chromis

2 Blue Devil

3 Threespot Dascyllus, juvenile

4 White Damsel

5 Behn's Damsel, adult *(top)*, juvenile *(bottom)*

6 Princess Damsel

BLUE DAMSEL
Pomacentrus pavo

The overall body colour of this species can change from a bright blue-green to a more subdued hue. There is usually a black spot behind the eye, blue lines on the head and dusky marks on the scales. It grows to a length of about 11cm (4¼in). *Ecology:* It occurs on reefs throughout the region and the wider Indo-Pacific, from shallow water to depths of about 16m (52ft). Individuals usually gather in small groups and are seen darting amongst corals. They feed mainly on zooplankton and filamentous algae.

SPECKLED DAMSEL
Pomacentrus bankanensis

This species is brownish with narrow blue lines on the head and also on the anal fin. The tail is pale and there is a blue-edged eye-spot towards the rear of the soft dorsal fin. It grows to a length of about 9cm (3½in). *Ecology:* It occurs on reefs throughout the region and in the western Pacific, from shallow water to depths of about 12m (40ft). It is usually found in rubble areas of the reef where it stays close to the bottom, browsing on algae.

DICK'S DAMSEL
Plectroglyphidodon dickii

The pale yellow body, white tail and dark bar towards the back of the body make this a fairly easily identified species. It reaches a length of about 11cm (4¼in). *Ecology:* It is found on reefs throughout the region and the wider Indo-Pacific, in shallow water to depths of about 12m (40ft). It is a territorial species and stays close to the reef surface, where it feeds on filamentous algae and small invertebrates.

WRASSE
Family Labridae

Wrasse are a very diverse group, with an enormous range in size and form. A characteristic is the way the pectoral fins are used in a rapid 'rowing' motion to propel them through the water. They typically have a fairly small terminal mouth with well-developed lips and one or more pairs of protruding canine teeth. Many species feed on bottom-dwelling invertebrates, especially shelled animals, such as molluscs, crabs and sea urchins. Special crushing teeth at the back of the throat (pharyngeal teeth) enable them to deal easily with hard or spiky food. *Thalassoma* spp. and juveniles of other wrasse are well known as cleaners, feeding on crustacean ectoparasites of other reef fish. Wrasse have a 'flexible' mating system that ensures spawning is likely to be successful under various circumstances. Most species begin their reproductive lives in a straightforward way, with females and 'initial phase' males, both of which have developed directly from juveniles. At this stage, the sexes are not easily distinguished by appearance. Subsequently, some of the females develop into 'terminal phase' males, which are colourful, larger and more territorial than initial phase males. These fish are usually territorial, and maintain a 'harem' of females. Around 150 species occur in the area.

DIANA'S HOGFISH
Bodianus diana

Juveniles have five or more white spots, arranged in rows, but some of these are lost as the fish matures. It grows to a length of about 25cm (10in). *Ecology:* It occurs on reefs throughout the region and the wider Indo-Pacific, from shallow water to depths of about 25m (80ft). It may be found alone or in small aggregations, and feeds on benthic invertebrates.

1 Blue Damsel

2 Speckled Damsel

3 Dick's Damsel

4 Diana's Hogfish

1 HARLEQUIN TUSKFISH
Choerodon fasciatus

Juveniles have brownish rather than red bars, and also have black spots on several of the fins. Like other species of *Choerodon*, the Harlequin Tuskfish has prominent, protruding canine teeth that are used to move aside pieces of rubble as the fish searches for molluscs or other invertebrates; teeth further back in the throat are then used to crush the prey. This species grows to a length of about 25cm (10in). *Ecology:* It occurs on reefs throughout the region and western Pacific, from shallow water to depths of about 15m (50ft). It is territorial but moves over a wide home range.

2 YELLOW-CHEEK TUSKFISH
Choerodon anchorago

The high forehead and yellow, black and white coloration of this species makes it easily recognized. It grows to a length of about 38cm (1ft 3in). *Ecology:* It occurs on reefs throughout the region and also the eastern Indian Ocean and western Pacific, from shallow water to depths of about 25m (80ft). It is usually solitary but occasionally small groups are seen.

3 BUMPHEAD or NAPOLEON WRASSE
Cheilinus undulatus

Juveniles are similar in colour to the adults, but lack the characteristic bump on the forehead. They can be distinguished from similar species by the presence of two short black lines behind the eye. The Bumphead is one of the largest of all reef fish, reaching a length of about 2.3m (7ft 6in). *Ecology:* It occurs on reefs throughout the region and the wider Indo-Pacific, from shallow water to at least 60m (200ft). Juveniles are usually found in shallower water, amongst corals, while adults are found deeper. An individual has a home range that normally incorporates a cave or large recess where it sleeps at night. Adults can tackle quite large, toxic and spiny prey, including Crown-of-thorns starfish.

4 TWO-SPOT MAORI or SPLENDOUR WRASSE
Oxycheilinus bimaculatus

This is a small wrasse, growing to a length of about 15cm (6in). It is similar to a number of other species, but can usually be positively identified by the shape of the tail fin, the dark stripe along the rear midline and the two small black spots on the body, one of which is on the front of the first dorsal fin, the other behind the pectoral fin. The male has a filament on the upper tail lobe. *Ecology:* It can be seen on reefs throughout the region and the wider Indo-Pacific, from shallow water to depths of over 100m (330ft), and usually in areas of rubble. It probably has a mixed diet, including small invertebrates.

5 CELEBES WRASSE
Oxycheilinus celebicus

The Celebes Wrasse can be identified by its beautiful coloration, and the longish nose with a slightly concave profile. It grows to a length of about 35cm (2ft 2in). *Ecology:* It is found on reefs throughout the region and in the western Pacific, from shallow water to depths of over 30m (100ft). It usually occurs singly, and stays fairly close to the reef surface where it searches for small invertebrates.

6 SLINGJAW
Epibulus insidiator

Juvenile Slingjaws are brownish with narrow white lines on the head and body, females are all-yellow, and males are darker with a white head. These fish get their name because of the way they can unfold the jaw to form a tube about half the length of the body. The suction created by this rapid movement draws small reef-dwelling fish and invertebrates straight into the mouth. It grows to about 35cm (1ft 2in). *Ecology:* It occurs on reefs throughout the region and the wider Indo-Pacific, from shallow water to depths of about 40m (130ft).

1 Harlequin Tuskfish

2 Yellow-cheek Tuskfish

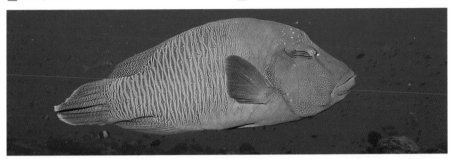

3 Bumphead *(top)*

4 Two-spot Maori *(above)*

5 Celebes Wrasse

6 Slingjaw

1 DRAGON or ROCKMOVER WRASSE
Novaculichthys taeniurus

The name Dragon Wrasse refers in particular to the juvenile, which blends perfectly with its surroundings, its filamentous fins mimicking seagrasses and seaweeds swaying to and fro. Adults lose the dragon-like appearance, are drabber in colour and are noted for their habit of turning over pieces of rubble to find food. It grows to about 25cm (10in). *Ecology:* It occurs on reefs throughout the region and the wider Indo-Pacific, from shallow water to depths of about 15m (50ft). It is mainly found in areas of sand and rubble, often on the back reef. It feeds on various invertebrates, including molluscs, crabs, worms and brittlestars.

2 BLACKSPOT RAZORFISH
Xrichthys dea

Juveniles are variable in colour, either dark or pale, but the adult is reddish, with indistinct bars and a black spot on the top of the back. This distinguishes it from the Blue Razorfish *X. pavo*, which also has a very elongated first dorsal fin. The Blackspot Razorfish grows to a length of 35cm (1ft 2in). *Ecology:* It occurs in sandy and seagrass habitats throughout the region, and also in the eastern Indian Ocean and west Pacific. It has a high, narrow forehead, which is thought to be an adaptation for plunging head-first into the sand. It does this when alarmed, then partially emerges and remains motionless with the head just showing. Benthic invertebrates make up its diet.

3 BLUESIDE WRASSE
Cirrhilabrus cyanopleura

There are numerous species of small, colourful *Cirrhilabrus* in the area, many of which are difficult to tell apart. The Blueside Wrasse reaches about 15cm (6in) in length and is one of the more distinctive, although the prominent blue patch is present only in the male. The female is pink. *Ecology:* It occurs on reefs throughout the region and also in the eastern Indian Ocean and west Pacific. Indi-

viduals swim in aggregations a few metres above the reef surface, feeding on zooplankton.

4 YELLOWTAIL WRASSE
Anampses meleagrides

The female of this species is easily recognized by the white spots and yellow tail. Males have a drab bluish body colour while the tail is yellowish with blue markings. Its maximum size is about 22cm (8½in). *Ecology:* It occurs on reefs throughout the region and wider Indo-Pacific, from shallow water to depths of about 60m (200ft). The juvenile is usually solitary, but females move around in groups with a larger male in the vicinity. They feed mainly on benthic invertebrates.

5 GAIMARD'S or YELLOWTAIL CORIS
Coris gaimard

Juvenile Gaimard's Coris are reddish orange with a white tail, two black-edged white spots on the head and three larger ones on the body. The adult, with its yellow tail, green streaks on the head and colourful body looks like a different species. It grows to a length of about 38cm (1ft 3in). *Ecology:* It occurs on reefs throughout the region and the wider Indo-Pacific, from shallow water to depths of about 50m (165ft), especially in areas of sand and rubble where it can be seen hunting for invertebrates.

6 YELLOW or GOLDEN WRASSE
Haliochoeres chrysus

There are many species of *Haliochoeres*, some of which are difficult to tell apart because their colour patterns are quite similar. The Yellow Wrasse is distinctive because of its bright yellow colour. The Canarytop Wrasse *H. leucoxanthus* is similar but has a white belly. The Yellow Wrasse grows to a length of about 12cm (4¾in). *Ecology:* It occurs on reefs throughout the region and in the eastern Indian Ocean and western Pacific, generally on patches of sand and rubble below about 20m (65ft) depth.

1 Dragon Wrasse, adult *(above)* and juvenile *(right)*

2 Blackspot Razorfish, juvenile

3 Blueside Wrasse

4 Yellowtail Wrasse

5 Gaimard's Coris, juvenile

6 Yellow Wrasse

1 CHECKERBOARD WRASSE
Haliochoeres hortulanus

Juveniles are black and white, females have a white bar behind the pectoral fin, but the male is greenish overall with red markings on the head and tail and two yellow spots on the back. It grows to a length of about 27cm (10½in). *Ecology:* It occurs on reefs throughout the region and the wider Indo-Pacific, from shallow water to depths of over 30m (100ft). It feeds on small invertebrates that it digs out of the sand.

2 FIVE-BANDED WRASSE
Hemigymnus fasciatus

The juvenile has a darkish body with narrow white vertical lines, while the adult is easily recognized by its black-and-white body and colourful patterning on the head. It grows to a maximum length of about 50cm (1ft 8in). *Ecology:* It occurs on reefs throughout the region and the wider Indo-Pacific, from shallow water to depths of about 40m (130ft). Juveniles feed on plankton and tend to gather close to branching corals, while adults hunt out bottom-dwelling invertebrates, mainly from rubble and coral areas.

3 BLACKEDGE THICKLIP WRASSE
Hemigymnus melapterus

The juvenile has a yellow tail, but otherwise has the similar division between black and white that easily identifies this species from a distance. The thick lips are an added identification feature. It grows to a length of about 50cm (1ft 8in). *Ecology:* It occurs on reefs throughout the region and the wider Indo-Pacific, from shallow water to depths of 30m (100ft). It feeds on benthic invertebrates and deals easily with shelled animals.

4 THREE-BLUELINE WRASSE
Stethojulis trilineata

Stethojulis species are small, highly mobile wrasse that can be difficult to distinguish. The male

Three-blueline Wrasse has blue lines on the head and body, and a distinctive red dorsal fin. Females are brown, yellow and white. This species reaches a length of about 14cm (5½in). *Ecology:* It occurs on reefs throughout the region and also in the central Indian Ocean and western Pacific. It is fairly uncommon, and is restricted mainly to the outer reef rim, from depths of about 3–20m (10–65ft).

5 SUNSET MOON WRASSE
Thalassoma lutescens

Thalassoma spp. are fast swimmers and amongst the most brightly coloured of wrasse. This is one of many present in the area and is easily recognized by its yellow body with red-and-blue markings. It grows to a length of about 30cm (12in). *Ecology:* It occurs on reefs throughout the region and the wider Indo-Pacific, from shallow water to depths of over 30m (100ft). It forages for small organisms in sandy, rubble and coral areas.

6 SIXBAR WRASSE
Thalassoma hardwicke

The male has black bars on a pale body, and bright red patterning on the head. It grows to a length of about 20cm (8in). *Ecology:* It occurs on reefs throughout the region and the wider Indo-Pacific, from shallow water to depths of about 15m (50ft).

7 BLUESTREAK CLEANER WRASSE
Labroides dimidiatus

Juveniles are darkish overall, with a single blue line along the side. Adults are pale or bluish with a dark line that widens towards the rear of the body. It grows to a length of about 11cm (4¼in). *Ecology:* It is common on reefs throughout the region and the wider Indo-Pacific, from shallow water to depths of at least 40m (130ft). Like a number of other wrasse, it feeds on external parasites of other reef fish. 'Clients' of all sizes come to 'cleaning stations' to be attended to, encouraging the wrasse to search inside their mouth and gills as well as on the outside of the body.

1 Checkerboard Wrasse

2 Five-banded Wrasse

3 Blackedge Thicklip Wrasse

4 Three-blueline Wrasse

5 Sunset Moon Wrasse (with Bluestreak Cleaner Wrasse above)

6 Sixbar Wrasse

7 Bluestreak Cleaner Wrasse

JAWFISH
Family Opistognathidae

These are small fish with a narrow body and long, continuous dorsal fin. The mouth is large and the jaws have a wide gape. Males incubate eggs in their mouth until ready to hatch.

1 GOLD-SPECS JAWFISH
Opistognathus sp.

The Gold-specs grows to 11cm (4¼in). *Ecology:* It is fairly common in Indonesia and the Philippines, and may be more widely distributed. It occurs from shallow water to depths of about 20m (65ft) in sandy areas where it constructs burrows reinforced with small stones and shell fragments. It may hover vertically above these when feeding, but if disturbed, rapidly retreats into the burrow tail-first.

PARROTFISH
Family Scaridae

Parrotfish are named after their teeth, which are fused into a beak-like structure. They use this when grazing on algae or biting corals to get at the soft parts inside. Feeding is incessant and often noisy. In addition, they leave visible scars on the reef limestone and on living corals. They are very important producers of sand, which comes from limestone that has been ground up in their gut. Parrotfish are hermaphrodites that function first as females, then as males. Usually the gaudiest individuals are the mature males. Parrotfish feed during the day and retire at night to hiding places under rocks and corals. Some secrete a mucous cocoon, which throws predators off their scent. There are probably about 30 species in the area.

2 BICOLOR PARROTFISH
Cetoscarus bicolor

The juvenile has a distinct colour pattern that is quite different from the greenish adult with its red lines and red edges to the scales. Juveniles are usually solitary, but adults move around in harems consisting of a male, female and several subordinates. They grow to length of about 80cm (2ft 7in). *Ecology:* It occurs on reefs throughout the region and in the wider Indo-Pacific, from shallow water to depths of over 30m (100ft).

3 BUMPHEAD PARROTFISH
Bolbometopon muricatum

The bump on the adult's forehead is very pronounced, and it is the only species with small raised bumps on the beak's outer surface. Juveniles have a steep head profile rather than a bump, and are brown with two rows of pale spots on the upper part of the body. This is one of the largest parrotfish, growing to about 1.3m (4ft 3in). *Ecology:* It occurs on reefs throughout the region and in the wider Indo-Pacific, from shallow water to depths of over 30m (100ft). These fish are an impressive sight as they move along the reef, releasing clouds of waste as they go, and stopping at intervals to bite at corals and rocks, sometimes head-butting them first to break them into chunks.

4 BLUEBARRED PARROTFISH
Scarus ghobban

Females are yellowish brown with four or five indistinct bluish bars while the male is an overall bluish colour with a distinctive wavy blue line under the eye. It grows to a length of about 75cm (2ft 6in). *Ecology:* It occurs on reefs and in sandy areas throughout the region and in the wider Indo-Pacific, from shallow water to depths of over 30m (100ft). Juveniles generally live in groups, but adults are usually solitary.

1 Gold-specs Jawfish

3 Bumphead Parrotfish

2 Bicolor Parrotfish, adult *(above)* and juvenile *(right)*

4 Bluebarred Parrotfish

REDLIP PARROTFISH
Scarus rubroviolaceus

Females are brownish with red on the head and the fins, and the male is bluish green with pink-and-blue marks around the mouth. It grows to a length of about 70cm (2ft 4in). *Ecology:* It occurs on reefs throughout the region and in the wider Indo-Pacific, from shallow water to depths of over 25m (80ft). Juveniles are usually single, but adults move around in pairs and sometimes join up with other species.

BULLETHEAD PARROTFISH
Scarus sordidus

Juveniles and females are brownish with four pairs of white spots on the side of the body, and a white tail base with a black spot in the centre. The male is bluish-green with pink-and-tan markings. It grows to a length of about 40cm (1ft 4in). *Ecology:* Occurs on reefs throughout the region and wider Indo-Pacific, from shallow water to depths of over 25m (80ft). Juveniles and females usually form groups and may travel widely for food.

BARRACUDA
Family Sphyraenidae

Barracuda are distinctive fish with elongate bodies, two widely separated dorsal fins and a forked tail. The head is pointed and the mouth large with a projecting lower jaw and long, sharp teeth. Barracuda are predators of other fish and can easily demolish their prey with a single bite. They are interested in divers, but the only circumstances in which they might attack are if people are spearfishing.

3 GREAT BARRACUDA
Sphyraena barracuda

This species is distinguished from others by its large size (up to 1.9m/6ft 3in), scattered dark markings along the body, tail fin with an almost straight margin, black second dorsal fin, and anal and tail fins with white tips. *Ecology:* It occurs in all tropical waters, in a wide range of habitats from bays to open sea and reef. Unlike some smaller species it is solitary by habit.

SANDPERCH
Family Pingupeidae

Sandperch are elongate fish with a long dorsal and anal fin and a distinctive pointed mouth with large lips. They are found mainly on sandy bottoms, and are active by day, feeding on small benthic invertebrates. About eight species occur in the area.

4 BLACKBANDED SANDPERCH
Parapercis tetracantha

All sandperch have bars on the body, but those in this species are darker and more pronounced than in others. Another identifying feature is the white-edged black spot between the eye and the dorsal fin. The Blackbanded Sandperch grows to a length of about 25cm (10in). *Ecology:* It occurs on reefs throughout the region, and in the eastern Indian Ocean and western Pacific. It is found on sand and rubble patches from shallow water to depths of about 20m (65ft).

1 Redlip Parrotfish with Remora attached *(top)*   2 Bullethead Parrotfish *(above)*

3 Great Barracuda

4 Blackbanded Sandperch

SAND-DIVERS
Family Trichonotidae

These extremely elongate fish spend most of their time hidden in the sand, sometimes with just the eyes showing. They emerge to feed, either resting on the surface or hovering in open water as they wait for zooplankton. Males are very distinctive, with long filamentous extensions to the dorsal fins that are used to ward off enemies and attract females.

1 BLUE-SPOTTED SAND-DIVER
Trichonotus setigerus

This is one of several species of sand-diver that occurs in the area. It is identified by the pale body

with its 12 indistinct brown bars. It grows to a length of about 15cm (6in). *Ecology:* It occurs in sandy patches on reefs throughout the region and the wider Indo-Pacific, from depths of about 3–40m (10–130ft). It is wary and dives into the sand if disturbed.

TRIPLEFINS
Family Tripterygiidae

These small blenny-like fish are readily identified by the three, separate dorsal fins. No other coral-reef fish have this feature. There are many species of triplefin, but most are difficult to identify underwater, and some are as yet undescribed. They feed mainly on small crustaceans.

2 NEON TRIPLEFIN
Helcogramma striata

This species is identified by the wide red stripes running along the body. It reaches a length of

about 4cm (1½in). *Ecology:* It occurs on reefs throughout the region and in the wider Indo-Pacific, from depths of about 5–30m (15–100ft). It lives on the surface of corals, sponges and other reef organisms, and feeds on tiny invertebrates.

BLENNIES
Family Blennidae

Blennies are small fish with an elongate, scaleless body and a single long dorsal fin. There are two major sub-groups within the family: the sabre-toothed blennies, with small mouths and big 'fangs' in the lower jaw, and the combtooth blennies with wide mouths and small teeth. The former are carnivores while the latter are mainly herbivores. There are over 300 species in tropical seas, and probably well over 100 in the South-east Asian region.

3 SCALE-EATING FANGBLENNY
Plagiotremus tapeinosoma

This fangblenny is identified by its stripes and the small yellow patch on the tail stem. It grows to 14cm (5½in). *Ecology:* It occurs on reefs through-

out the region and in the wider Indo-Pacific, from shallow water to depths of about 20m (65ft). Like other fangblennies, it feeds on skin and scales of other fish, and will also bite divers. It usually rests in old worm holes, with just the head showing, darting out to feed and moving through the water with a characteristic wiggling motion of the body.

1 Blue-spotted Sand-diver

2 Neon Triplefin

3 Scale-eating Fangblenny

1 BLUESTRIPED FANGBLENNY
Plagiotremus rhinorhynchos

This species grows to 12cm (4¾in) and is either brown with narrow blue stripes or has alternate blue-and-black stripes. The latter colour pattern resembles that of the cleaner wrasse, *Labroides dimidiatus*. This mimicry allows the fangblenny to get close to unsuspecting fish, which instead of being cleaned have a bite taken out of them. They have even been known to bite divers. *Ecology:* It occurs on reefs throughout the region and in the wider Indo-Pacific, from shallow water to depths of about 40m (130ft). It lodges in old worm holes on the reef in between forays for food.

2 BICOLOR BLENNY
Ecsenius bicolor

This species is easily recognized by its blue front and yellow rear – most other blennies are much more difficult to identify. It grows to a length of about 10cm (4in). *Ecology:* It occurs on reefs and in rocky areas throughout the region, and in central Indian Ocean and western Pacific, from shallow water to depths of about 25m (80ft).

3 LEOPARD BLENNY
Exalias brevis

The male of this species is beautifully coloured, with patches of red spots all over the body and most fins. It grows to a length of about 14cm (5½in). *Ecology:* It occurs on reefs throughout the region and in the wider Indo-Pacific, from shallow water to depths of about 20m (65ft). It lives on branching coral and feeds on the coral polyps. Eggs are also laid on the coral, after the male has prepared a suitable nest site by grazing away the polyps. Several females deposit eggs in the nest, the male fertilizes them and then guards the nest against predators.

4 BANDED BLENNY
Salarius fasciatus

This species has indistinct vertical bands, with fine dark lines running along the body. It reaches 14cm (5½in) in length. *Ecology:* It occurs on reefs throughout the region and in the wider Indo-Pacific, from the reef flat to depths of about 6m (20ft). It feeds on algae and is generally seen in shallow areas with rubble and rock where algae thrive.

DRAGONETS
Family Callionomidae

Dragonets are small fish with two dorsal fins and prominent eyes on top of the head. The first dorsal fin in the male is normally large and colourful, and is used as an advertisement during spawning. There is a large spine on the cheek and the skin is tough, scaleless and covered with a distasteful mucus. The gill opening, rather than being a slit, is a small hole. Dragonets live in sandy or rubble habitats where they feed on small invertebrates. Many are pale or mottled and blend in well with the background, but a few are very flamboyant.

5 MANDARINFISH
Synchiropus splendidus

This is one of the more spectacular species of dragonet and grows to a length of about 6cm (2¼in). The Picturesque Dragonet *S. picturatus* is equally colourful but has a pale greenish body with yellow-edged green circles on the body rather than the black-edged red lines on a dark green body. *Ecology:* The Mandarinfish occurs on coastal, often silty reefs mainly in the east of the region and also in the western Pacific, at depths of about 3–30m (10–100ft). It usually hides in amongst coral or rubble, so is difficult to spot despite its bright colours.

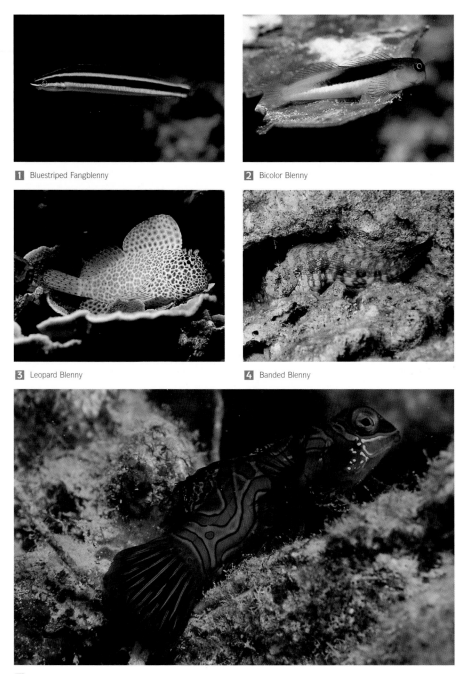

1 Bluestriped Fangblenny

2 Bicolor Blenny

3 Leopard Blenny

4 Banded Blenny

5 Mandarinfish

FINGERED DRAGONET
Dactylopus dactylopus

This species gets its name from the separate finger-like, first ray on each pelvic fin. The dorsal fin is also very prominent and is raised when the fish is disturbed. It is mottled to match its surroundings, and grows to a length of about 18cm (7in). *Ecology:* It occurs in sandy habitats at a range of depths from shallow water to over 50m (165ft). It may be buried during the day.

DARTFISH
Family Microdesmidae

Dartfish are small elongate fish with a short first dorsal fin and a longer second one. The anal fin is also long. They live in pairs or groups and spend much of the day time hovering above the reef surface feeding on zooplankton. At any sign of danger they quickly dart into burrows in the sand or holes amongst coral and rubble. About eight species occur in the region.

2 DECORATED DARTFISH
Nemateleotris decora

This species is recognized by its pale body, colourful fins and purplish nose. The anterior spines on the first dorsal are longer than the others and are often held upright. It reaches a length of 9cm (3½in). *Ecology:* It occurs on reefs throughout the region and in the Indian Ocean and western Pacific, on sandy or rubble areas, generally below 20m (65ft) and to at least 70m (230ft).

3 BLACKFIN DARTFISH
Ptereleotris evides

This species is identified by its two-tone colour. It is the largest of the dartfish, growing to a length of approximately 14cm (5½in). *Ecology:* It occurs on reefs throughout the region and in the wider Indo-Pacific, from shallow water to depths of about 15m (50ft). It is usually seen hovering 1–2m (3–6ft) above its hole, feeding on plankton.

GOBIES
Family Gobiidae

Gobies are small fish with elongate bodies and two dorsal fins. Most are bottom dwellers and tend to rest on their pelvic fins, which may be modified into a small cup-like suction disk. Such species mainly feed on small invertebrates on the reef surface, but others swim in open water and capture plankton. Gobies are abundant in sandy areas, and some associate with other reef animals. Several hundred species probably occur in the South-east Asian region.

4 STEINITZ'S PRAWNGOBY
Amblyeleotris steinitzi

This species has brown bars on a pale background and grows to about 8cm (3in). *Ecology:* It occurs in sandy habitats on reefs throughout the region and in the Indian Ocean and western Pacific, from shallow water to depths of 5–28m (15–90ft). Like other prawngobies, it lives in burrows in a symbiotic relationship with a blind or nearly blind prawn. The prawn does all the digging while the goby acts as the lookout, and warns its compatriot of danger.

1 Fingered Dragonet

2 Decorated Dartfish

3 Blackfin Dartfish

4 Steinitz's Prawngoby

1 SPOTTED PRAWNGOBY
Amblyeleotris guttata

The orange spots and black markings enable this species to be fairly easily identified. It grows to a length of about 9cm (3½in). *Ecology:* It occurs in sandy habitats on reefs in the east of the region and out into the Pacific Ocean, from shallow depths of about 10–35m (33–115ft).

2 MAIDEN or ORANGE-DASHED GOBY
Valencienna puellaris

This species has a pale body and fins with a row of orange dashes along the side and orange spots above. It grows to a length of about 17cm (6¾in). *Ecology:* It occurs on coarse sand habitats throughout the region and in the wider Indo-Pacific, at depths of about 15–20m (50–65ft). It lives in a burrow but is not associated with prawns. Like others in the same genus, it forages during the day, biting several centimetres down into the sand and then sifting the material over its gill rakers, removing small crustaceans, nematodes, foraminiferans and other items of food.

3 ORANGE-RED GOBY
Trimma okinawae

An unknown number of *Trimma* species occur in the area, and many of them are undescribed. The Orange-red goby is identified by the densely packed reddish-orange spots on the body and fins. Like others in the genus, it is very small, reaching a maximum length of 4cm (1½in). *Ecology:* It occurs on reefs throughout the region, usually in crevices or caves. It feeds on small bottom-dwelling animals.

4 FINE HAIR PYGMY GOBY
Eviota prasites

This is another example of one of the numerous small gobies that occurs in the area. It is one of the more brightly coloured *Eviota* species, and grows to a length of about 2cm (¾in). *Ecology:* It occurs on reefs throughout the region and in the western Pacific.

MOORISH IDOL
Family Zanclidae

This is one of the few families that contains only a single species. It is closely related to surgeonfish, but lacks the blades at the tail base and also has a more tubular snout.

5 MOORISH IDOL
Zanclus cornutus

The shape and colour patterns of the Moorish Idol mean that it is occasionally mistaken for a bannerfish, but the tubular snout with its orange mark are very distinctive. It reaches a length of approximately 16cm (6¼in). *Ecology:* It occurs on all types of reef throughout the region and in the wider Indo-Pacific, from shallow water to depths of about 200m (660ft). Members of this species usually move around in small groups, but occasionally they form large aggregations. Sponges form an important part of their diet.

1 Spotted Prawngoby

2 Maiden Goby *(above)*

3 Orange-red Goby *(left)*

4 Fine Hair Pygmy Goby

5 Moorish Idol

SURGEONFISH AND UNICORNFISH
Family Acanthuridae

Surgeonfish have an oval, compressed body, small mouth and a long, continuous dorsal fin. They get their name from the scalpel-like spine on each side of the tail stem. These are used both for offence and defence, including territorial defence against others of their own species. Many surgeonfish are herbivores and often feed in the shallowest regions of the reef front; others feed on plankton. Unicornfish (*Naso* species) are distinguished by having fixed spines (one or two) on the tail stem, rather than ones that fold away. Some, but not all, have a 'horn' on the front of the head, which gives this sub-group its name. Most unicornfish form small groups or schools on steep outer reef slopes or drop-offs where they feed primarily on zooplankton. Around 40 species of acanthurids occur in the region.

1 BROWN or BRUSHTAIL TANG
Zebrasoma scopas

There are several *Zebrasoma* species in the area, all of which have enlarged dorsal and anal fins, thus giving the common name sailfin tang. Juveniles have narrow vertical lines but adults are brownish with a white spine at the tail base. It grows to a length of about 20cm (8in). *Ecology:* It occurs on reefs throughout the region and in the wider Indo-Pacific, from shallow water to depths of about 60m (200ft). The Brown Tang often moves around singly, but sometimes forms small groups. These fish are constantly on the move, pausing briefly but frequently to pick at algae on the surface.

2 POWDER-BLUE SURGEONFISH
Acanthurus leucosternon

The bright colour pattern of this surgeonfish is very distinctive. The Palette Surgeonfish *A. hepatus* is also blue, but has black marks on the body rather than the head, and has a yellow tail. The Powder-blue grows to a length of about 23cm (9in). *Ecology:* It occurs on reefs throughout the region and in the Indian Ocean and western Pacific, from very shallow water to depths of about 25m (80ft). They sometimes form very large aggregations, especially on shallow areas of oceanic reefs. When grazing in these large groups they are a formidable force, easily overwhelming territorial damselfish trying to guard their own particular patch of algae.

3 STRIPED SURGEONFISH
Acanthurus lineatus

This is the only surgeonfish in the area with yellow and blue stripes. Like many other territorial fish, it can alter the intensity of the colours to match its mood. Whilst grazing or patrolling its territory undisturbed, the blue and yellow stripes are slightly muted, but when excited or aggravated, the stripes stand out more brightly and a white patch appears on the central part of the tail fin. It grows to a length of about 38cm (1ft 3in). *Ecology:* It occurs on reefs throughout the region and the wider Indo-Pacific, from the surge zone to a depth of about 4m (13ft). The largest fish is male, and each has a territory with a harem of females. The boundary of adjacent territories is sometimes marked by a 'hedgerow' of uncropped algae, which grows freely in 'no-man's land'.

4 YELLOWMASK SURGEONFISH
Acanthurus mata

This species can also change colour in an instant, from a pale greyish blue to a much darker hue. The yellow mask around the eye is usually visible, although several other species also have this feature. The Yellowmask Surgeonfish grows to a length of about 50cm (1ft 8in). *Ecology:* It occurs around reefs throughout the region and in the wider Indo-Pacific, generally in shallow water, where it forms small groups some distance up from the reef surface. The adults feed on zooplankton and the juveniles on benthic algae.

1 Brown Tang

2 Powder-blue Surgeonfish

3 Striped Surgeonfish

4 Yellowmask Surgeonfish

1 GOLDRING BRISTLETOOTH
Ctenochaetus strigosus

Several similar species of *Ctenochaetus* occur in the region. Most are brownish in colour with fine lines or dots. The Goldring Bristletooth has yellow spots on its head and and usually a yellow ring around its eye. The juvenile is mostly yellow. It grows to a length of about 18cm (7in). *Ecology:* It occurs on reefs throughout the region and in the wider Indo-Pacific, from shallow water to depths of over 45m (150ft). It is often seen in small groups picking at algae on the reef.

2 SLEEK or BLACKTONGUE UNICORNFISH
Naso hexacanthus

This is one of several species of unicornfish that does not have a horn. The sleek body shape is dis-

tinctive, and the larger individuals (males) have black margins to the gill covers and also a black tongue. It grows to a length of about 60cm (2ft). *Ecology:* It occurs throughout the region and in the wider Indo-Pacific, mainly on outer reefs, from depths of about 6m (20ft) to more than 130m (425ft). It feeds on large zooplankton.

3 SPOTTED UNICORNFISH
Naso brevirostris

Despite the name *brevirostris*, the horn on this species is long and prominent. The body is brownish with spots and there is a distinctive wide, white band behind the head. Its maximum length is about 60cm (2ft). *Ecology:* It occurs on reefs throughout the region and in the wider Indo-Pacific, from shallow water to depths of about 45m (150ft). Juveniles graze on algae, while the adults feed on zooplankton up in the water column.

RABBITFISH
Family Siganidae

Rabbitfish are medium-sized, deep-bodied fish with a single dorsal fin. They have a distinctive small mouth with close-set teeth that are used for grazing, which is presumably how they got their name. These fish occur only in the Indo-Pacific, where they are common inhabitants of lagoonal areas, especially seagrass beds and algal-covered limestone outcrops. They feed mainly on algae but may also pick at attached organisms, such as seasquirts and sponges. At least 12 species occur in the area.

4 MASKED RABBITFISH
Siganus puellus

The Masked Rabbitfish is similar to a number of other rabbitfish in having blue markings on a yellowish body. It is best distinguished by the single bar through the eye and the yellow forehead. Its maximum length is about 38cm (1ft 3in). *Ecology:* It occurs on reefs throughout the region and in the eastern Indian Ocean and western Pacific, from shallow water to depths of about 30m (100ft), where it feeds on algae, sponges and tunicates.

5 LINED RABBITFISH
Siganus lineatus

Both the Golden Rabbitfish (*S. guttatus*) and the Lined Rabbitfish have a large yellow spot below the soft dorsal fin. However, the two are easily distinguished by the body markings: spots in *S. guttatus* and lines in *S. lineatus*. Both species grow to a length of about 42cm (1ft 5in). *Ecology:* The Lined Rabbitfish occurs on reefs throughout the region and in the eastern Indian Ocean and western Pacific, mainly in shallow protected areas. It feeds on sponges and algae.

Rabbitfish

1 Goldring Bristletooth

2 Sleek Unicornfish

3 Spotted Unicornfish

4 Masked Rabbitfish

5 Lined Rabbitfish

TUNA
Family Scombridae

Tuna are quite large, silvery fish with two dorsal fins and a series of tiny finlets behind the anal and second dorsal fins. They are fast swimmers with a streamlined body and forked tail. Many occur in the region, but they prefer the open ocean and only visit reefs occasionally.

DOGTOOTH TUNA
Gymnosarda unicolor

The Dogtooth Tuna is silvery with white tips to the second dorsal and anal fins. It reaches a length of about 1.9m (6ft 3in). *Ecology:* It occasionally visits steep lagoon and seaward reefs, occurring throughout the region and the wider Indo-Pacific, from shallow water to depths of about 100m (330ft). It is an active fish predator.

FLOUNDERS
Family Bothidae

Flounders are flatfish that have both eyes on the left side of the body. The eye from the right side migrates around as the fish develops from the free-swimming, upright juvenile to take up a bottom-dwelling existence. Only one or two species are seen on or around reefs.

PEACOCK FLOUNDER
Bothus mancus

This species can change colour rapidly to blend in with its background, but the blue marks do not fade completely. The upper rays on the pectoral fin of the male are very elongate. Its maximum length is about 42cm (1ft 5in). *Ecology:* It occurs in sandy areas on and around reefs throughout the region, and the wider Indo-Pacific, from shallow water to depths of over 80m (260ft).

TRIGGERFISH
Family Balistidae

Triggerfish have fairly deep, compressed bodies with eyes set high on the head. They get their name from the large first dorsal spine, which can be erected and then locked into place. Triggerfish feed on shelled animals, such as crustaceans, molluscs and sea urchins, which they crush with their powerful jaws and teeth. A few feed on plankton. Most triggerfish have conspicuous colour patterns and so are easily picked out. They also have a curious way of swimming, by undulating the anal and second dorsal fins, bringing in the tail for extra speed.

RED-TOOTHED TRIGGERFISH
Odonus niger

The dark blue body and long filaments on the tail are diagnostic. Its length is about 40cm (1ft 4in). *Ecology:* It occurs on seaward reefs throughout the region and the wider Indo-Pacific, from shallow water to depths of about 40m (130ft). It typically occurs on steep current-swept sites where it feeds mainly on zooplankton. If disturbed it dives for safety head-first into a crevice where it wedges itself in with the dorsal fin spine, leaving nothing visible except the outer margin of the tail.

1 Dogtooth Tuna *(top)*　　**2** Peacock Flounder *(middle)*　　**3** Red-toothed Triggerfish *(bottom)*

1 ORANGE-LINED TRIGGERFISH
Balistapus undulatus

The orange lines are very distinct and are best developed in the female. They are still present in the male, but generally absent from the snout. It grows to a length of about 30cm (12in). *Ecology:* It occurs on reefs throughout the region and in the wider Indo-Pacific, from shallow water to depths of about 50m (165ft). It feeds on a wide range of reef organisms, including sponges, corals, echinoderms, crustaceans and even fish.

2 TITAN or MOUSTACHE TRIGGERFISH
Balistoides viridescens

The Titan is similar to the Yellowmargin Triggerfish *Pseudobalistes flavimarginatus*, but can be distinguished by the lack of yellow margins to the fins and the presence of dark 'moustaches' above the upper lip. The Titan is the largest triggerfish in the area, growing to a length of 75cm

(2ft 6in). *Ecology:* It occurs on reefs throughout the region and in the wider Indo-Pacific, from shallow water to depths of about 40m (130ft). Juveniles are generally found in shallow, sheltered parts of the reef, but adults occur in a range of habitats. These fish spawn in a depression in the sand, which they clear and prepare by removing pieces of rubble with their mouth. After spawning, the female cares for the eggs while the male patrols the territory. At this time they are very aggressive to intruders and will attack divers with ferocity and without warning.

3 PICASSO TRIGGERFISH
Rhinecanthus aculeatus

This is one of several *Rhinecanthus* species that occur in the area, but it is easily recognized by the complex patterns and two white saddles on the back. It grows to a length of about 25cm (10in). *Ecology:* It occurs on reefs throughout the region and in the wider Indo-Pacific, mainly in sandy or rubble areas in shallow water. It feeds on algae, detritus and a wide range of invertebrate animals.

FILEFISH AND LEATHERJACKETS
Family Monacanthidae

Filefish are closely related to triggerfish, but have a longer, thinner first dorsal spine that cannot be locked up. They may have hairs or small spines on each side of the body, just in front of the tail stem. Over 20 species occur in the area.

4 SCRIBBLED FILEFISH
Aluterus scriptus

The Scribbled Filefish has a characteristic body shape, with an elongate tail. The body colour varies, but there are always blue lines and spots, with a scattering of black spots. It reaches a maximum length of about 1.1m (3ft 7in). *Ecology:* It occurs in tropical waters throughout the world, and is usually seen drifting over reefs about a metre above the bottom. It occurs from shallow water to depths of about 80m (260ft) and feeds on a range of reef organisms includ-

ing algae, seagrass and gorgonians. The juvenile is pelagic and associates with floating algae.

5 BLACKLINED FILEFISH
Pervagor nigrolineatus

Confusingly, this species has a distinct white mark on the side of its body and the fine black lines that give it its name form a rather indistinct background. It reaches a maximum length of about 10cm (4in). *Ecology:* It occurs on reefs throughout the region and in the western Pacific, from shallow water to depths of about 25m (80ft).

1 Orange-lined Triggerfish

2 Titan Triggerfish

3 Picasso Triggerfish

4 Scribbled Filefish

5 Blacklined Filefish

1 BLACK-SADDLE MIMIC
Paraluteres prionurus

This leatherjacket grows to a maximum length of 10cm (4in), and has an almost identical coloration to the Black-saddled Toby (*see* p.138). It can be distinguished by the presence of two dorsal fins, the first of which has a strong spine. In addition, the anal and second dorsal fins are longer than in the pufferfish. *Ecology:* It occurs on reefs throughout the region and in the wider Indo-Pacific, from shallow water to depths of about 25m (80ft). It moves around singly or in small groups, and is left alone by potential predators because of its near perfect mimicry of a poisonous species.

2 SMALL-SPOTTED LEATHERJACKET
Pseudomonacanthus macrurus

This species has many very small spots, and an overall mottled appearance, but it can change its appearance rapidly to match its background. It reaches a maximum length of about 24cm (9½in). *Ecology:* It occurs in Indonesia and the eastern part of the region, down to Australia. It inhabits broad-leaved seagrass beds and weedy habitats from shallow water to depths of about 15m (50ft), where it feeds on small invertebrates. It is well camouflaged and may be overlooked.

TRUNKFISH
Family Ostraciidae

These fish get their name from the bony plates that encase the head and body. The shell is inflexible and is often adorned with ridges and spines. There are small gaps for the mouth, eyes, gill openings, anus and fins. Trunkfish are predators on a range of small invertebrates. Most live in territories consisting of a dominant male with several females and sub-adults. Apart from their protective armoury, many trunkfish also secrete toxic substances when alarmed or threatened. These can be lethal to other fish, especially in the confines of an aquarium.

3 LONG-HORNED COWFISH
Lactoria cornuta

As its name implies, this species has very long horns. It also has a long tail, which increases proportionally with age. It is one of the larger trunkfish, reaching a length of over 45cm (1ft 6in). *Ecology:* It occurs on reefs throughout the region and in the wider Indo-Pacific, from shallow water to depths of about 50m (165ft). It feeds by blowing a stream of water at the sand to excavate a hole and unearth small prey, especially crustaceans. Wrasse often follow them around, looking for an easy meal.

4 SPOTTED BOXFISH
Ostracion meleagris

Juveniles and females are black with small white spots. The fish are hermaphrodites, and females develop into males, which are blue with yellow spots. These larger individuals reach a length of about 20cm (8in). *Ecology:* It occurs on reefs throughout the region and in the wider Indo-Pacific, from shallow water to depths of about 30m (100ft). It feeds on sponges and small reef invertebrates.

1 Blacksaddle Mimic

2 Small-spotted Leatherjacket

3 Long-horned Cowfish

4 Spotted Boxfish

PUFFERFISH
Family Tetradontidae

Pufferfish are named after their ability to puff up their bodies in self defence by drawing water through the mouth into a special chamber near the stomach. They have tough, prickly skin that is greatly stretched during this process until the fish resembles a small football. To deter predators even further, they also contain a powerful toxin in the viscera, gonads and skin. Pufferfish have a mixed diet, including algae, and both hard- and soft-bodied invertebrates. They hide at night and are active during the day. Divers should never chase or annoy them in order to try and make them inflate. There may be as many as 100 species in the region.

BLACK-SADDLED TOBY
Canthigaster valentini

This species can be confused with the Blacksaddle Mimic (*see* p.136). The Crown Toby *C. coronata* also has a similar colour pattern but has shorter saddles that do not reach onto the belly as they do in the Black-saddled Toby. The latter reaches a length of about 10cm (4in). *Ecology:* It occurs on reefs throughout the region and in the wider Indo-Pacific, from shallow water to depths of about 55m (180ft). It is a territorial species and the male has a harem of females, spawning with a different one each day.

FALSE-EYE PUFFER
Canthigaster papua

This species is distinguished from the very similar Spotted Toby *C. solandri* by the longitudinal lines on the tail stem and upper body. It grows to a length of about 10cm (4in). *Ecology:* It occurs in Indonesia and the western Pacific, overlapping with the Spotted Toby, which has a more widespread distribution throughout the Indo-Pacific. It is found at depths of about 5–50m (15–165ft) in a variety of habitats. Its food consists mainly of algae, but also includes reef invertebrates.

MAP PUFFER
Arothron mappa

The pattern of spots and dashes on this puffer are quite variable, but it can usually be identified by the dark lines that radiate out from the eye. It is a large species, reaching a length of about 65cm (2ft 2in). *Ecology:* It occurs on reefs throughout the region and in the wider Indo-Pacific, from shallow water to depths of about 30m (100ft). It has a mixed diet, including algae, sponges and reef invertebrates.

PORCUPINEFISH
Family Diodontidae

Porcupinefish are very similar to pufferfish. The main difference is that the body is covered in sharp spines (modified scales), which become erect when the body is inflated. They have hard, beak-like jaws well adapted for crushing shelled animals, such as molluscs, crustaceans and sea urchins. There are about 20 species in the region.

BLOTCHED PORCUPINEFISH
Diodon liturosus

The black blotches distinguish this from other porcupinefish. It grows to a length of about 45cm (1ft 6in). *Ecology:* It occurs on reefs throughout the region and in the wider Indo-Pacific. Juveniles are usually found in shallow water, but adults occur down to depths of about 90m (300ft). It generally rests during the day and emerges at night to feed.

1 Black-saddled Toby

2 False-eye Puffer

3 Map Puffer

4 Blotched Porcupinefish

TURTLES

Of the seven species of marine turtle found throughout the world, six can be found in the South-east Asian region. Although these reptiles spend long periods submerged, they have to come to the surface to breathe, and females also make their way onto land to lay eggs. When struggling up the beach to nest they look ungainly, yet underwater they are magnificent and powerful swimmers. The shell gives good protection, but sometimes bears scars – perhaps from encounters with boat propellers or with their only natural predator, the shark. If they can avoid these hazards and reach maturity, turtles are long-lived. They may not reach sexual maturity until they are well over 20 years old, and then they may live to be over 100 years old. Due to the many pressures on turtles, all species are listed in Appendix I of the Convention on International Trade in Endangered Species, which prohibits all international trade.

1 HAWKSBILL TURTLE
Eretmochelys imbricata

This species is distinguished by its pointed head, hawk-like beak, and overlapping bony plates on the back. The richly coloured and patterned shell has been the Hawksbill's downfall because of its value for jewellery and objects, such as spectacle frames. The Hawksbill occurs on coral reefs worldwide at depths of 40m (130ft) or more, and feeds on attached reef organisms, particularly sponges and soft corals, which it rips apart with great determination.

DOLPHINS

These warm-blooded, intelligent mammals are a welcome sight as they play alongside boats or visit the reef, but their real domain is out in the ocean, catching fish. A dolphin's sense of smell and taste is not well developed, and their eyesight is relatively poor. However, they make up for this by having a highly sensitive 'echo-location' system, which enables them to pick up sounds, locate prey and understand precisely what is going on around them.

2 SPINNER DOLPHIN
Stenella longirostris

This is one of the most frequently seen dolphins in the region. Markings are very variable, but they are easily recognized by the slim build and long nose. They usually move around in large schools, and are stimulated by the sound of boats – exploding into action and leaping out of the water as they surge forward. They often approach boats and 'bow-ride', seeming to enjoy the sensation of water flow and turbulence as the boat moves forward. They generate clicking sounds and squeals to 'talk' to each other underwater, and occasionally are heard by divers, but it is not easy to get close. Spinner Dolphins feed on squid and small fish, hunting to depths of 100m (330ft) or more.

1 Hawksbill Turtle

2 Spinner Dolphin

GLOSSARY

Aggregation: individuals gathered together in a loose group. Can apply to fish or to attached animals.

Anal fin: single fin running along the underside of a fish, from the anal opening towards the tail.

Benthic: dwelling on the seabed, either attached or unattached.

Colony/colonial: animal that consists of numerous similar or identical 'units' (e.g. polyps) that are linked together to form the complete organism.

Commensal: relationship in which two species live in close physical association, and are dependent on each other for some function or other.

Dorsal fin: fin running along the top of the body in the mid-line; it may be single or split into two or three separate sections.

Hermaphrodite: individual that contains both ovaries and testes in its body. These may be functional at the same time, or the animal may function first as one sex and then the other.

Ectoparasite: animal that lives on the outside of another, and is dependent on it for its nutrition (e.g. it attaches to the skin and feeds on blood).

Invertebrates: animals without backbones.

Omnivorous/omnivores: animals with a diet consisting of a mixture of plant and animal material.

Herbivorous/herbivores: animals that feed on plants, such as algae and seagrasses.

Plankton: plants (phytoplankton) or animals (zooplankton) that float in the water column and are

moved by ocean currrents. Mainly microscopic, but includes larger organisms, such as jellyfish.

Pectoral fins: pair of fins located one each side of the body, just behind the head.

Pelagic: living and swimming in the water column, rather than close to or on the seabed.

Pelvic fins: pair of fins located on the underside of the fish, usually beneath the pectoral fins.

Predator: animal that hunts and feeds on other animals.

Symbiotic: relationship in which two (or more) species live together and benefit each other in one or more ways.

Territory: living, feeding or breeding area that is actively defended from intruders by the inhabitant(s).

INDEX